The AIRCRAFT COCKPIT

Patrick Stephens Limited, part of Thorsons, a division of the Collins Publishing Group, has published authoritative, quality books for enthusiasts for more than twenty years. During that time the company has established a reputation as one of the world's leading publishers of books on aviation, maritime, military, model-making, motor cycling, motoring, motor racing, railway and railway modelling subjects. Readers or authors with suggestions for books they would like to see published are invited to write to: The Editorial Director, Patrick Stephens Limited, Thorsons Publishing Group, Wellingborough, Northants, NN8 2RQ.

THE
AIRCRAFT COCKPIT

from stick-and-string to fly-by-wire

L.F.E. COOMBS

FOREWORD BY BILL GUNSTON

Patrick Stephens Limited

First published in 1990

British Library Cataloguing in Publication Data
Coombs, L.F.E.
The aircraft cockpit: from stick-and-string to fly-by-wire.
1. Aircraft, history
629.133'09

ISBN 1-85260-281-3

Endpaper illustrations Cockpit evolution, from the Breguet wheel and rudder bar
system of about 1912, fitted to a dual control machine (front) to the 'digital' flight deck
of Airbus A320 (rear). (*Photos via Aeroplane Monthly, and Airbus Industrie*)

Patrick Stephens Limited is part of the Thorsons Publishing Group,
Wellingborough, Northamptonshire NN8 2RQ, England

Typeset by Burns & Smith Limited, Derby
Printed in Great Britain by Butler & Tanner Limited,
Frome, Somerset

1 3 5 7 9 10 8 6 4 2

In memory of all those pilots
whose problems were compounded
by the inadequacies of their
cockpit.

CONTENTS

FOREWORD

by BILL GUNSTON

I have known Les Coombs since the early 1950s. In those days I was a pilot, and of course familiar with panels filled with dial-type electromechanical instruments. Today I am much more familiar with what we call 'glass cockpits' and it is quite a shock to notice how far we have come. Nobody, for my money, could tell the story better than Les.

The story is much more than the mere development of 'instruments'. When the Wright brothers were playing with biplane gliders in the first three years of this century they merely lay prone on the lower wing, working their body from side to side in order to warp the wings for the world's first lateral control (which other would-be aviators had completely overlooked). When they built their powered Flyer they again lay on the wing, but offset to one side to balance the weight of the engine. Since then most pilots have sat in some kind of seat, though in the immediate post-war era several aircraft were modified for what were called prone-piloting experiments. This throwback to the Wrights was intended to combat g (acceleration in the vertical plane) by putting the body across the imposed forces instead of in line with them.

Today the fighter pilot adopts exactly the opposite posture. Instead of lying on his tummy he sits in a seat inclined backwards so that he is almost lying on his back. His head, tilted forwards, is encased in a complex dome which increasingly contains synthetic electronically created images in his line of sight. Without doubt it will soon be possible to dispense with external vision entirely. I have read several reports positively advocating this. It would eliminate eye damage caused by lasers, and the absence of transparent glass or plastics would eliminate glint in sunshine which can betray the aircraft's presence at a distance.

To us oldies it seems like yesterday that fighter pilots were furiously arguing over the relative merits of open and enclosed cockpits. Many experienced pilots insisted that you had to be able to crane your neck and look astern, below and everywhere else (and if you want to survive in air combat that's just what you have to do), and they were adamant that confining them inside a rigid canopy was going to prove a grave handicap. I wonder what they would have said to being confined inside an *opaque* canopy?

Unlike the much simpler task of designing the controls of a car — where, such is the lack of standardization, if ever I drive either of my daughters' cars, I work the wipers when I mean to indicate a turn — the designers of cockpits have pretty well ironed out the dangerous inconsistencies that caused so many crashes in the past. In World War Two it was not uncommon for pilots to land and then select gear up instead of flaps up, and there are countless instances of silly design in such things as fuel cocks and tank selectors. Only occasionally today does the designer have to ponder on a cockpit problem.

One that comes to mind was the GD Fort Worth team's difficulty in 1963–64 in deciding how to arrange the wing-sweep control of the F–111. The wings are forward at low speeds and swept back for high speeds, but traditionally you push everything (such as the throttles) forward for maximum speed. In the end they chose to use a linear sliding device descriptively called a trombone lever, and made it go forward to sweep the wings back. Over the years several pilots have got it wrong. In my view they should have made the lever a miniature wing, moving through an arc of degrees of sweep. Like that you surely couldn't get it wrong?

Even traditional cockpits are often full of unexpected problems. Perhaps most people would think a Viscount was a Viscount; but in 1969 British Midland were in such trouble with their Viscounts that angry passengers were unable to depart despite the fact there were both Viscount captains and serviceable Viscounts! They eventually grouped their V.760, 831 and 833 variants into one Fleet, and qualified captains on those three types, and the V.702, 755, 785, 814 and 815 into a second Fleet, and qualified different captains on all those. I do not believe anyone was required to qualify on the lot. This sort of thing might not occur even to 'Viscount enthusiasts', but it can mean the difference between life and death.

The pilot's place has inevitably always been a life-or-death place – though sharply differing in degree of danger – and though it is often still called 'the office' it is very much more demanding than most offices. This book needed to be written, and it is both entertaining and an important and often instructive historical record.

Bill Gunston
Haslemere, Surrey

INTRODUCTION

The cockpits of the pioneering years of aviation, 1903 to 1955, are fading into the past. The cockpits of the future are emerging from the present.

Before the past disappears it is worthwhile recording some of the more important and some of the less important, even frivolous, ideas which have led to today's cockpits and flight decks. 'In the right hand of God was the control column and at his feet the rudder bar', a paraphrase which, up to 15 years ago, seemed to be carved in stone, no longer applies. Each year the changes, both actual and predicted, become greater.

Many of the arrangements of the flight decks and cockpits of today have their origins in the first twenty or so years of powered flight. Just as steam replaced sail at sea, but without abandoning completely some of the control practices and equipment of earlier years, so the modern jet aircraft still exhibits traces of earlier times. In the last ten years, however, there have been some revolutionary changes in the cockpit.

The number of different aircraft types essayed or built since 1903 exceeds 2,000. Any history of the cockpit must therefore be a selective review among the many different types of aircraft. Recourse has to be made to 'typical examples'. Nevertheless certain types warrant special mention, either because they have unusual control positions or introduced new features which became worldwide standards.

The author apologizes to those whose favourite aircraft type has either been neglected or dismissed with only few words, but space is limited. The helicopter cockpit is not included. Although an attempt has been made to give equal attention to civil and military aviation it has been necessary to devote proportionally more space to the cockpits of the two world wars. This has been done because in those years there was rapid growth in aircraft performance and complexity which required corresponding additions and improvements to the pilot's place.

It is important to emphasize that this book is not intended as a design manual.

The primary control position of an aircraft, be it a rudimentary cockpit or the flight deck of Concorde, has always been the focus of interest from the early years of powered flight to the present. For many, it has been — and still is — their goal in an aviation career; for others, it is a fascinating world of instruments and controls; for the dramatist, it is indeed the seat of high drama. In no other means of transport are life or death reactions and decisions called for, not in minutes, but in split seconds. The captain of a ship has usually some minutes, often ten or twenty, in which to steer away from danger; the driver of a train has a simplified control decision problem which essentially is that of exercising a stop action in response to a danger signal; the driver of a car, admittedly has to exercise on occasions the split-second reaction to events of the aircraft pilot, but is rarely directly responsible for hundreds of lives or for the destiny of a nation. The 'world' of the aircraft pilot imposes a particular and in many ways unique set of control and decision tasks.

Now and then the not very attractive word 'ergonomics' — the study of man in his working environment and of ways of improving (equally unattractive) the man-machine interface, such as the aircraft cockpit — is used. Forty years ago few knew of the word (something to do with economics?); today it even appears in advertisements for new cars. It is unfortunately one of those words that has to be used ... another is the term 'human factors' ... and there are others.

Development of the pilot's place is still continuing at a pace. So many new ideas emerge each week that to try and keep up with them would mean making additions up to the last minute before printing. Therefore, the reader is requested to accept the limitations of keeping 'up-to-date' and not be surprised to read of 'future' cockpit technologies which are already in service.

The pilot's place has evolved from being nothing more elaborate than a simple seat among the struts and wires of the early flying machines to the modern flight deck and cockpit. During the 80 years of evolution, instruments in particular have proliferated since about 1930, until by the 1950s they had reached considerable numbers on the larger types of aircraft; so many in fact that pilots under stress were not always able to scan and absorb all the information presented. At the same time instruments, particularly those classified as primary flight, were at the limit of the electro-mechanical systems designer's skill. A point in evolution was reached at which the number of pointers, numeral counters and flags could no longer be increased or their display characteristics improved.

This is not intended as a book on the history of aircraft instruments as such. Instruments are a separate subject and the bibliography recommends a number of studies. But they cannot be ignored, because they form, along with the controls, an important element of any cockpit.

The contribution made to the efficiency of the cockpit as part of the relationship between pilot and aircraft changed significantly in the 1960s when the CRT (cathode ray tube) display became available. The CRT, in conjunction with the digital computer, altered the look of the pilot's place nearly out of recognition. In place of serried ranks of individual instruments came the colour CRTs. As few as six CRT screens now provide all the essential information needed to control and monitor a flight.

Obviously, the cockpit, which forms one of the most important parts of an aircraft, cannot be studied in isolation. In the same way the pilot and the cockpit are related to the total operating environment. Once radio became a reliable method of communication the pilot was no longer operating a vehicle independently of others. His world now embraced far more than the cockpit and his range of vision.

The 'isolated' pilot concept gradually faded away with the growth of communication and navigational aids. It lingered on in remote areas and pleasure flying. This is one reason why any study of the cockpit has to be more than just a list of equipment and its position.

Today few pilots can have the pleasure of jumping in, switching on and taking off into the 'wild blue yonder'. A flight must be planned, notified and approved. Specified tracks and heights must be adhered to with precision. If an air traffic controller says over the radio, 'Turn left onto one eight zero', the pilot does not

The first cockpit? Leonardo Da Vinci's flying machine. (Mike Oakey)

question the command because he knows that it is based on information which is not necessarily available in the cockpit. Even a planned take-off may be denied and the pilot, crew and passengers must sit patiently and wait while someone else sorts out conflicting departure traffic. As we all know, to our frustration, a departure time can depend on air traffic thousands of miles away. Which all goes to show that the authority of the pilot in command has changed over the years even if the responsibility remains.

In 1909 it was stated: 'It would be an exaggeration to say that anyone can drive a Voisin aeroplane, but it is not going beyond the confines of truth to declare that any sportsman, especially a man familiar with motoring, cycling, ballooning or yachting, can learn to fly in half an hour. The designers have made their apparatus as automatic as possible, trying to eliminate the human element and thus giving the maximum of security.' Yet despite when that was written, it contains ideas which span over 80 years of con-

trollable, powered, heavier-than-air flight. The references to 'as automatic as possible' and 'eliminating the human element' would not be out of place in the descriptions of aircraft being designed for the year 2000.

Throughout the history of aircraft development there has been a succession of instruments and systems designed to ease the pilot's task and to make the most effective use of the pilot's abilities, with more automatic systems to take the muscle work out of flying and more accurate and informative instruments being introduced from time to time. The human element in the cockpit or on the flight deck is just as important today as it was in 1903: man's faculties have hardly changed over the eighty or more years of man-controlled heavier-than-air flight. Today's pilots come from a generation which is familiar from an early age with computer and electronic display technology, so that the modern flight deck with its displays does not seem strange; all the same, little can be done to enhance the general physical and mental abilities of pilots in general. The cost of training them to the standards of astronauts would be prohibitive. The pilot cannot therefore be further refined. Which means that we have to develop better and better systems for the flight deck which will enable the pilot to remain in control despite increasing workloads and, in military flying, increasing stress and hazards.

Electronic displays driven by digital computers have already eased the pilot's workload. With each new generation of aircraft from about 1970 the number and quality of the electronic displays steadily increased, along with the versatility and power of the associated computers. Between 1970 and 1990 there occurred perhaps one of the most revolutionary phases in cockpit evolution. Before about 1970 improvements in the civil aircraft flight deck had been evolutionary rather than revolutionary, with only occasional advances such as the artificial horizon, other 'blind' flying instruments, radio navigation instruments, automatic pilots, weather radar, pointer-counter presentations and inertial navigation control and display panels.

In addition to the encouragement given to the development of engines of ever increasing reliability, power and efficiency and to structural materials and aerodynamics, the needs of aviation contributed much to the development of electronics for communication, navigation and detection. As early as 1910, for example, Robert Loraine, flying a Boxkite over British Army exercises, sent the Morse signal 'Enemy in sight'.

The cockpit, as a setting for drama, introduces the subject of aviation films, and the many misrepresentations as well as the engendering of a number of misconceptions about the pilot and cockpits in general.

The external, inward-looking, shot which enables the audience to see the actor's face is one of the most frequently used in aviation films. In those involving the flying of single-seat fighters, the external camera position which takes in the windscreen and canopy as well as the pilot's head and shoulders, with a background of sky and earth, has proved acceptable. However, when the scene is that of a two-pilot flight deck, the audience is often aware of the fact that the nose of the aircraft, plus most of the controls and instruments, has had to be removed. The overall effect is unreal. Of course, it is always easy to criticize, particularly if the difficulties of camera position, sound equipment and lighting in the cramped confines of a cockpit are ignored.

Modern video equipment permits inflight 'shooting' and produces realistic 'in the cockpit' action, which is why some old aviation films appear even more contrived and artificial than they appeared to contemporary audiences whose expectation of realism was much less than that of today's viewers. Except for documentary films, the 'star' quality of a film has always been more important than technical accuracy. When film producers in general have been questioned about their choice of a particular aircraft type they have replied 'An aircraft is an aircraft is an aircraft. Does it matter?' Aircraft and their cockpits, like ships and trains, have often changed type from scene to scene.

As with the authors of some novels, so film producers and directors are not always up to date with technology. Although most anxious to include death rays, they have often failed to include essential details.

Writers of aviation films and books have a tendency to embrace the adage 'Don't let the facts spoil a good story'. The most notable 'convenience' is the way fictional pilots are able to leap into the cockpit, press the starter button, wave away the chocks and go roaring off. All this is in sharp contrast to the need in a real aircraft to select and operate a number of controls and make various checks ... even in a 1940s type 'scramble'.

The gathering of facts and examples on which this book is based is something that started many years ago. An interest in the design of control systems for all types of vehicles and experience of many different types of aircraft began to coalesce in the 1950s. This was encouraged by two technical press editors in particular, Bill (W.T.) Gunston and Mike (J.M.) Ramsden of *Flight International*, who took a chance on an article of mine which they published under the title they gave it of 'The Pilot's Place'. Without their early inspiration this book may never have appeared in print. Bill Gunston also provided many useful comments on my early drafts and has always been helpful in reminding me of a number of important facts relating to aviation.

This book also has its origins in the deliberations of the Technical Committee of the British Air Line Pilots Association. The committee chairman at one time was Captain M.W. Broom, who did much to further the interests of pilots in the design of their place of work. There were, of course, many others. As secretary to the committee I learnt much about the good and the bad in cockpit design from pilots of considerable experience and monumental patience. Of course, 'good and bad' is a simplification. Few flight decks were so bad that none would use them, and few were so good that they set standards for others. In those formative years, the 1950s, of pilot opinion on the subject of the design of the pilot's place there were wide differences among the various aircraft types. This was not just because some were propeller-driven and the others jets but because of the lack of standardization of instruments and cockpit equipment.

During many years of sticking my neck out by commenting on cockpit design I have made many friends who are also interested in the subject, and there have been others whose acquaintance has only been through correspondence. To all I am most grateful. To mention just a few, I will start with Dr J.M. Rolfe, who at the time he was with the RAF Institute of Aviation Medicine encouraged me to formalize my studies of the cockpit along academic lines. We met by chance because of arguments in the press over that black sheep among instruments, the three-pointer altimeter.

Two others with whom I had the pleasure of discussing the subject are Dick (R.J.) Chorley, an authority on both the design and the history of aircraft instruments, and Professor Elwyn Edwards, whose academic career in human factors included first-hand experience of flying civil aircraft on scheduled services.

I must also mention the encouragement and help of Dr Helen Muir and Mike Hirst of the College of Aeronautics at Cranfield, with whom I have had many interesting discussions on the future design of the flight deck and control of aircraft. This subject also introduced me to Professor John Allen, one time head of future aircraft design at British Aerospace, Kingston.

Richard Riding, editor, and Mike Oakey, of *Aeroplane Monthly* are others who must be thanked for considerable help with the preparation of this book. Along with Don Middleton and John Stroud they made possible a large proportion of the illustrations – many of which are absolutely essential.

Another editor who encouraged the writing of articles about the cockpit is Gordon Swanborough of Pilot Press. Mike W. Wilson has over the years been another who has encouraged my interest in the subject and who on many occasions has applied his skilful editor's blue pencil to my manuscripts.

Many aviation companies and organizations have contributed information and illustrations. Among them I must mention the great help received from David W. Bainbridge and Keith Dougan of Smiths Industries, whose products form such an important part of American and British flight decks and cockpits. I must also mention John Coombs, Greg Ferguson, David

Charlton, Dave Clark and Allan Piper of British Aerospace, Derek James, author and editor of *Wingspan*, Mike Ottewell of Ferranti, Dr R.J. Braune and Dick Kenny of Boeing, Malcolm Moulton of GEC Avionics, David Vellupilai of Airbus Industrie, Brian Wexham of Vickers plc, Sperry Ltd, Martin Baker, Air Cdre F.B. Yetman and Mr S. Lane of BALPA, the RAF Museum, and Helmets Ltd. A particular mention must be included for the help received from Kollsman USA, who provided much useful information on early instrument flight equipment. All responded to numerous requests for information and pictures.

The opinions expressed, and any errors, are my own.

CHAPTER ONE

1903

17 December 1903, Orville Wright settled himself prone on the lower wing of the Wright Flyer. Alongside lay the four-cylinder Wright engine: its furious exhaust crackled at his right ear. Behind him rattled the chain drives from the engine to the two propellers whose blades spun round. A bitterly cold winter gusted over the sand dunes and round the side of the low Kill Devil Hills.

On the previous attempt it had been Wilber's turn to fly, so now it was Orville's turn at the controls. Perhaps with hindsight and with our present experience of technology, 'controls' is not the most appropriate word: there were only a few levers; as for instruments, they were also few in number.

Orville lay with his hips in a cradle. This was the important wing-warping control. By moving his hips towards the desired direction of a turn, the cradle, which was connected to the trailing edges of the outer wing panels, warped the wings so as to produce greater lift on one side and less on the other. The warping cradle was also joined to the twin rudders at the stern. Pitch, that most important control of all for an aircraft intended to fly in close proximity to the ground, was

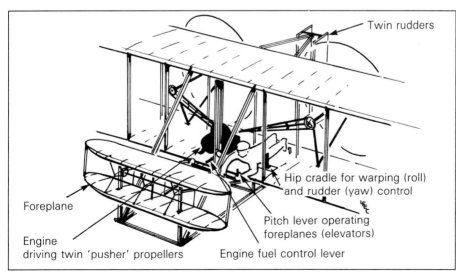

Foreplane

Engine
driving twin 'pusher' propellers

Twin rudders

Hip cradle for warping (roll)
and rudder (yaw) control

Pitch lever operating
foreplanes (elevators)

Engine fuel control lever

*Wright Flyer of 1903
with prone pilot
position.* (Author)

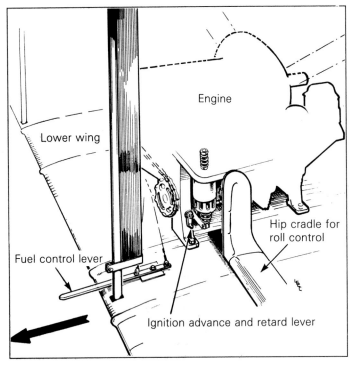

Labels on image:
Engine
Lower wing
Fuel control lever
Hip cradle for roll control
Ignition advance and retard lever

Wright Flyer of 1903: engine controls. (Author)

engine would not have been sufficient to overcome the resistance to forward motion of the four to five square feet of the pilot's body.

Without a suitable engine the Wright Flyer literally would not have got off the ground. So what about the engine controls? There was one, and one only, unless you include the fuel cock from the overhead tank. The engine had virtually only one speed: flat out. The only control used by the pilot was the advance and retard lever for the ignition system.

Orville Wright pulled the release cable which tethered the machine. Slowly the Flyer gathered speed along the launching rail. His left hand held the pitch lever ready to counter the effects of the turbulent air caused by the 23-knot wind as it tumbled over the dunes and low hills.

At the time, Orville Wright could not be aware that history was about to be made. He had other things to think about. The flight was most erratic because of the turbulent air at low level. His biggest problem arose from a design fault: the elevators were overbalanced; in other words, they were hinged too close to their centre. Once they were moved they tended to go on moving, thereby overcontrolling and adding to the pilot's task. After 12 seconds, a combination of overbalanced controls, pilot inexperience and a down gust ended the flight as the Flyer slithered to a standstill on the sand.

Instruments were used for this and the following series of flights. But these were as recorders rather than aids to the pilot. An anemometer drove a two-pointer indicator of distance covered. A pilot-operated stop watch was used to time the flight. An engine revolutions counter recorded the number of turns made by the propellers. These different readings were combined to determine both the distance and speed of the flight. Otherwise there were no instruments.

The average speed of each of the flights made in December 1903 was about 30 mph; the Wright Brothers did not therefore think it necessary to discard

effected by a 'biplane' pair of forward elevators. A rod from the elevators went directly to a lever at the pilot's left hand. The movement of this pitch lever was unambiguously arranged: lever forward to lower the nose; back to raise the nose. This was a simple and what might be called an 'expected' arrangement because it acted in a natural way. Nevertheless subsequent control arrangements by both the Wright brothers and other aviation pioneers would nowadays be rejected because their direction of movement was neither natural nor expected. 'Cockpit' is really too far-fetched a word to describe the position of the pilot, his controls, his instruments, or his immediate surroundings. Orville lay exposed to the elements. The Wright Flyer I was purely functional: fabric stretched over wooden ribs; bare structural members; all these components braced by numerous wires. The engine, like the pilot, lay on the lower wing exposed to the airstream. Both pilot and engine represented unwelcome drag. Had the pilot sat upright, the power of the

Farman Type 3. The control wires attached to the top of the control column at the pilot's right-hand will remain slack until the machine gains speed and the ailerons and elevators lift up to their flying position. (via Aeroplane Monthly)

their high stiff white collars. A more important detail in the light of subsequent events: they did not use any restraining harness. Indeed those were carefree days.

The pilot

Before tracing the principal evolutionary steps which have led to the modern flight deck, it is appropriate to say something about that most important item of cockpit equipment – an item which was installed in the Wright Flyer of 1903 and is still to be found in today's 'front office': the human pilot.

The history of aviation includes that special relationship which developed between man and machine. Before there were aircraft, man had become accustomed to controlling horses and ships and, at the time of the Wrights' historic flight, was just acquiring automobile driving skills. Man took to the air and exercised control of a flying machine by using his natural senses of balance and direction. The subsequent history of aviation, particularly that of the pilot's place, is marked by a series of milestones of technology concerned with instruments and equipment developed to enable the human pilot to remain in control in all conditions of flight.

The early flying machines and many of those which followed over the next 80 years were symmetrical in plan form and were designed to give the pilot symmetrical freedom of control around the three axes of roll, pitch and yaw. But in practice there have been many examples of aerodynamic, mechanical and human preferences which have made it easier to control an aircraft, particularly in roll and yaw, in one direction rather than in the other.

The cockpit, or flight deck, is, to use some jargon, the interface between man and machine. That interface therefore has to cope with human hand and side preferences. For example the majority of pilots are and always have been, like the rest of the population, right-handed.

Perhaps the most significant example

Valkyrie pusher monoplane circa 1910: right hand on stick, left on throttle. Just visible inboard of the violin-shaped upright panel on the pilot's left is the vital oil pulsometer indicator glass bulb. (via Aeroplane Monthly)

Bleriot Monoplane circa 1909. The rods projecting upwards from the fuel tanks in front of the pilot's map are attached to cork floats to indicate how much is in the tanks. (via Aeroplane Monthly)

of hand preference influencing both the design of a cockpit and the manoeuvring of aircraft is the 'right hand on stick, left on throttle' arrangement of the majority of single-engine aircraft cockpits. Although in the ten years after 1903 there were examples of 'left hand on stick, right hand on throttle': Bleriot's 1909 'Channel Crosser' was one.

Even before the successful flights by the Wright Brothers in 1903, many of the less successful inventors of flying machines were concerned primarily with developing aerial craft which would be inherently stable. In other words one which would 'ride' the air 'waves' like a ship: a machine which if left to its own devices would continue on its original path.

Experience with model aircraft convinced the Wrights that a flying machine, if it were to be successful, had to have neutral stability or a slight degree of instability. This meant that the pilot had to maintain continuous control of the craft at all times. Although the idea of a fully stable craft, like a ship, seemed the logical choice, nevertheless such an arrangement would make an aircraft difficult to manoeuvre.

From this fundamental concept emerged the long tradition of the pilot with his hands and feet on the controls for the majority of the time. Of course, many aircraft types when flying in calm air could be flown 'hands off' for some time.

Primary controls

Primary controls using hands and feet evolved during the first decade of heavier-than-air flight: hands for aileron (roll) and elevator (pitch) control; feet for control of the rudder (yaw). Unlike in ships and many steam locomotives, a standing position was not adopted for the pilot. Still, it might have been otherwise, for during those pioneering years, many different types of primary control were tried, not all requiring the intervention of

the pilot's feet. Whichever particular lines of evolution were, or might have been, adopted, the need to reduce the frontal area of an aircraft predicated either a prone or seated position for the pilot.

Few tasks in the history of transport and machines in general can match that of the human pilot. The three-dimensional environment (roll, pitch, yaw) in which an aircraft is flown is, in many respects, unique; only in recent times has it been emulated by the submarine. The three-dimensional world of flying and the unfortunate basic law that 'What goes up must come down' introduce hazards for the pilot which he is not likely to meet in any other form of vehicle.

The speed with which events occur when flying has always required the highest application of human abilities and in particular the ability to react quickly and correctly: there are no second chances in aviation.

The nature of the pilot's world is such that his survival and that of those entrusted to his care depends on the exercise of extreme caution at all times. There is not, and never has been, any room for carelessness, inattention or recklessness. Although facetious, there is much truth in the expression, 'There are young pilots and bold pilots but few old, bold pilots.' An exception is the air force pilot in time of war when called upon to exercise boldness in performing operational tasks, but at all other times he is trained to act with caution, if for no other reason than that aircraft are expensive and pilots are expensive to train. The transport, passenger and working aircraft pilot has always had to resist the temptation to 'press on' and thereby take risks.

In those parts of this book which cover specific aircraft and cockpit types there are many examples of failures on the part of the designers to understand fully the work and needs of the human pilot. In the more general context of events, during the First World War pilots had to perform reconnaissance patrols for two or

Demoiselle at a meeting at Bournemouth in 1910. In the event of a crash, the pilot arrived first! (via Aeroplane Monthly)

three hours at a time. When flying close to 20,000 feet without oxygen and without any form of heating they were subjected to a combination of many tasks in a tiring and hostile environment. On landing, they were often too exhausted to give a clear report of what they had observed. With the war at an end, all this type of flying stopped. This was good for the pilots but not necessarily good for the future design of aircraft cockpits, because any research which had got under way directed at improving the lot of the pilot also stopped. Admittedly electrically-heated flying suits and oxygen masks had been introduced in order to sustain some semblance of life above 15,000 feet. But any studies into cockpit design in general came virtually to a halt. They would not be restarted until the mid 1920s.

For many years cockpits were given far less design consideration than other parts of an aircraft. For the risk of exaggeration, the typical designer first worried about the major bits such as engine, fuel tanks and guns, and only then looked for a place in which to seat the pilot. Even if a designer started with the cockpit, it was still only considered to be a space of suffi-cient volume (and no more) in which to fit the pilot and all his equipment.

Designers of earlier years would some-times decide on the major dimensions of a new aircraft by drawing it in chalk on the hangar wall or on the floor. As they com-pleted their preliminary scheme each per-formed the fundamental design of keeping the major weights as close to the centre of lift as practicable. In aircraft like the Camel and Snipe, the pilot, his heavy flying clothing, his seat, controls, in-struments and other equipment was a significant part of the aircraft's all-up weight and therefore had to be kept close to the centre of lift.

With aircraft in mid-World War One having an all-up weight of around 1,500 lb, the 200 lb of the pilot and his equipment plus 150 lb for each gun and ammunition represented nearly a quarter of the take-off weight.

It is fair to say that from 1903 till about 1930 those responsible for the position, shape and equipment of the cockpit worked to the following order of priorities:

1. Yes, we must find a place for the pilot, and like the other heavy items let us

keep him close to the aircraft's centre of lift.

2. Yes, we will give him a seat and we will make sure that the principal controls are within reach of his hands and feet.

3. Yes, we will provide some instruments, or at any rate those which are available. But we cannot guarantee that the pilot will have all the instruments he will need for all the different circumstances of a flight.

4. No, we cannot arrange and position all the secondary controls, such as fuel cocks and switches, in a logical order or within the undistorted reach of the pilot's fingers.

5. Many of the things the pilot might like to have cannot be included because they will increase the aircraft's weight above the design limits.

6. In designing the aircraft, and its cockpit in particular, we place great reliance on the special abilities of the pilot. Pilots have been trained to overcome difficulties and they do seem to like dressing up in thick leather coats, wearing silk scarves and helmets with goggles.

The last item may have been exaggerated but in general pilots themselves preferred to brave the elements and therefore were averse to being confined within an enclosed cockpit. Many items of equipment both inside and outside the cockpit, such as radio aids to landing, were not immediately acceptable to all pilots. Only the economic pressures in civil aviation for the need to operate to a schedule irrespective of weather and visibility conditions forced the general acceptance of equipment designed to help the pilot.

When new ideas were introduced to help the pilot to maintain control when the ground and horizon were invisible, they were introduced one by one and therefore, for example, there was no co-ordinated arrangement of instruments.

Early Controls

The Wright Brothers had demonstrated practical powered, controllable flight,

The evolution of the primary controls. (Author)

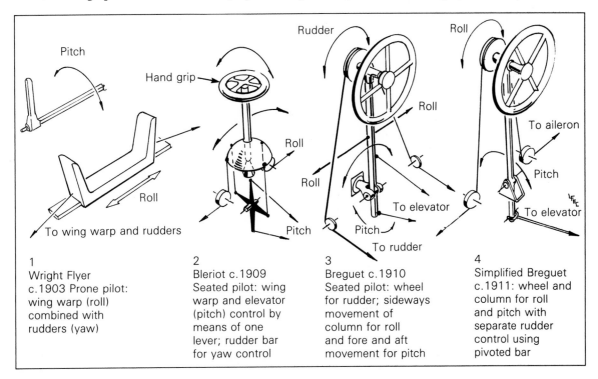

1
Wright Flyer
c.1903 Prone pilot: wing warp (roll) combined with rudders (yaw)

2
Bleriot c.1909
Seated pilot: wing warp and elevator (pitch) control by means of one lever; rudder bar for yaw control

3
Breguet c.1910
Seated pilot: wheel for rudder; sideways movement of column for roll and fore and aft movement for pitch

4
Simplified Breguet c.1911: wheel and column for roll and pitch with separate rudder control using pivoted bar

but their basic method of control was not adopted as the international standard. Between 1903 and 1914 many different types of primary control were tried. There were nearly as many different arrangements of control columns, wheels and levers as there were pioneer airmen. Yet one pioneer had a lasting influence on cockpit design. This was the Frenchman Louis Bleriot. He designed and flew a successful tractor propeller monoplane with a system of control markedly different from that of the Wright Brothers.

Bleriot's patent No. 2588 of 1908 describes a control column mounted in a form of Carden joint, operating controlling surfaces at right angles to one another, so that lateral movement of the column operates warp, and fore-and-aft movement operates the elevators.

In addition, the Bleriot Monoplane had a rudder bar. To the early aviators the rudder bar might have seemed to be operating in the wrong sense when compared with the handlebars of a bicycle. Two explanations for this arrangement are: one, that the rudder is akin to that of

a boat, in effect having the tiller wires running forward to the helmsman where they are operated by the pilot's feet in the same sense as the hand movements of a coxswain; or two, that on the early types of aircraft, designers preferred to keep the rudder control linkage in tension when operating, so that the system pulled rather than pushed, thereby compensating for any airframe flexure. Of course, the wires could have been crossed to produce a more natural sense of control. And, indeed, as late as 1910 there were examples of rudder bars connected so as to operate in the same sense as the handlebars of a bicycle.

The Bleriot Monoplane was used at a number of flying schools prior to the First World War. Its 'conventional' controls, consisting of stick and rudder bar, were adapted by other designers, so that, with the expansion of military aviation as the war got under way, this basic method of control became the standard for aircraft on both sides of the conflict.

Bleriot's engine controls mounted on the joystick may have been inspired by

Wright dual-control circa 1911: an example of mixed primary controls. The pilot in the left seat used the lever at his right hand to effect control of both the rudders and the wing warping; the lever at the left hand was used to control the elevators. This particular aircraft was also equipped with rudder bars. Not a particularly easy set of control relationships for an ab initio pilot to master. The set of controls for the instructor was what we would now term conventional. (via Aeroplane Monthly)

contemporary automobile practice – particularly as the top of the column was fitted with a small 'steering wheel'. However, this wheel was only a convenient hand grip and had no operating function.

Bleriot's compatriot Breguet introduced a variation of the former's control. This had a wheel for operating the ailerons in place of the sideways movement of the stick. Incidentally the Breguet control system at that time did not include a rudder bar: the rudder was automatically co-ordinated with the ailerons. When used with independent rudder control the Breguet method became the standard for large aircraft. However, the division between 'joystick' and 'wheel' aircraft is not a precise one; some small aircraft have had a wheel and some large aircraft, such as the Vulcan bomber of the 1960s, a stick.

In the later Wright machines the pilot

Above *A foot-operated throttle (the foot belonging to an American, Blanche Scott) circa 1910. No rudder bar in this Curtiss Canard biplane. (via Aeroplane Monthly)*

Left *Bleriot's 'cloche' control for roll and pitch: the 'steering' wheel had no function other than to provide a convenient hand grip. (via Aeroplane Monthly)*

By about 1912 the Wrights had abandoned their unique method of primary control and had adopted the Breguet wheel and rudder bar system, as fitted to this dual control machine. (via Aeroplane Monthly)

sat on the leading edge of the lower wing and used his two hands for control but not his hips.

In the pioneering days of flight, and for the next ten years, the cockpit remained either as a seat among the bracing wires or as a low-sided 'sheltered depression in the deck'. The achievement of longer flights, as engine reliability improved, and the development of more effective control systems left designers little time in which to worry about the comfort of the pilot. As it happened, the designer was usually the pilot, so he had no one to blame but himself if he found his aerial perch wet and draughty and somewhat lacking in instruments.

Operating environment

In dealing first with the general shape and structure of the pilot's place, the term 'pilot's place' is used deliberately to avoid the repetitious use of either 'cockpit' or 'flight deck'. These two terms are often used indiscriminately, cockpit often being preferred for single-seat layouts and flight deck for multi-crew control stations. In the USA 'flight station' is sometimes used.

As a digression, the word cockpit seems to have derived from the nautical terminology for an opening in the upper deck of a yacht intended to give some protection to the helmsman. There is also the earlier use of the word for one of the lower compartments of a wooden sailing ship in the navy. The 'some protection' part of the description was most appropriate in the first decade of powered flight because little or no protection was afforded the pilot. But then the speeds achieved by the early aircraft were not much different from those experienced by the drivers of cars. Furthermore the pioneer aviators did not fly particularly high and if they were able to wrap up warmly enough for take-off then that sufficed for the remainder of the flight.

It may seem somewhat out of context to introduce the subject of pilots' clothing, but an important characteristic of the curve of technical evolution of the pilot's place is the steady improvement in

Left *A pioneering British airman, Gordon England, with cap on back to front and baggage stowed behind his seat — his back cushion cover a Union flag* (via Aeroplane Monthly)

Below *E. Austin-Hurson, who gained the first international pilot's certificate. The helmet and goggles appear to have been the only concession to wearing suitable clothing for flying!* (via Aeroplane Monthly)

the pilot's working environment. Essentially we can describe this as from fur-lined flying suits, sometimes with electrical heating, helmet and goggles, to today's shirt-sleeve environment of the civil cockpit.

Vision

The ability to see forward, downward, upward, and in fact all round an aircraft, was a significant feature of early aviation, when the pilot sat exposed to the elements. In more recent times, because of structural and aerodynamic factors, this had tended to become an impracticable wish on the part of pilots.

For the first ten years of powered, heavier-than-air flight, the pilot invariably was able to see over wide arcs of vision in both the horizontal and vertical planes. The hard facts of flying in those days emphasized the need to use the human eye as an essential part of the control interface. There were no flight in-struments, so pilots had to maintain stable flight and keep to a desired course by reference to the line of the horizon and to ground features. These features could be referred to on a map and suitable corrections made to the aircraft's heading in order to maintain the desired course to the destination. Over featureless terrain and over the sea aviators had to use the dead-reckoning procedures of the mariner, but over land and given good visibility, navigation could proceed by frequent reference to prominent ground features. In those days the idea of sitting in a completely enclosed cockpit and with only a narrow view of the outside world would have been laughed at. Even 30 years after the Wright Brothers' 1903 flight many pilots preferred to have their heads exposed above the upper line of the fuselage.

Undoubtedly the small glass windscreen was considered an essential minimum item of protection in even the earliest types of enclosed fuselage air-

Anthony Fokker at the controls of his first aircraft, with excellent views in all directions; the only instrument to be seen, that attached to his thigh. 'Cockpit' is hardly the right word to use. (via Aeroplane Monthly)

Bleriot Monoplane used for the London to Paris flight in 1911; note the roller map, and the two instruments plus pulsometer alongside. (via Aeroplane Monthly)

Daily Mail Circuit of 1911: J. Valentine in his Deperdussin Monoplane. The engine controls are on the control yoke; fuel tank pressurizing pump at the pilot's right hand; direct reading glass tube contents indicator on sloping surface of fuel tank; roller map case to hand. (via Aeroplane Monthly)

Below *The pilot's place in a Farman Boxkite. This photograph includes interesting details such as the domestic light switch for controlling the ignition, the simple method of connecting the dual-control columns, the 'master' fuel cock alongside the two-person seat and, on the strut to the right of the seat, the oil system pulsometer.* (via Aeroplane Monthly)

Opposite page above *Another view of a Deperdussin — a two-seat version, with Captain Hamilton of the RFC in command and instruments and*

craft. Even military aircraft retained a small glass screen despite the need to find room for forwardly aligned sights for aiming the guns. Complete enclosure of the cockpit of single-seat aircraft did not become a standard feature until aircraft operating heights reached 20,000 feet or more. At this height oxygen was essential equipment, as well as an enclosing canopy to enable a pilot to operate efficiently at high altitude. It is interesting to note that the completely enclosed cockpit presented a considerable design problem because of the difficulties of producing curved, laminated transparent panels, such as perspex or glass. At first only single-curvature panels could be made, and it was not until the late 1930s that double-curvature transparent panels reached the production stage.

Early instruments

In the beginning all was confusion, except of course on a calm, sunny, cloudless day when the pilot's instinctive reactions to movements of his machine, along with his view of the horizon and the ground, enabled him to exercise effective control.

Early instruments were sometimes just pieces of string to indicate sideslip, but the most important 'instrument' was the feel of the slipstream on the pilot's cheeks. The 'wind on the cheek' became a vital factor which remained of value for over two decades. It also contributed to the retention of the open cockpit. Completely enclosed, a pilot was deprived of this useful indication of sideslipping either inwards or outwards during a turn. Not until the turn and slip indicator was introduced in the early 1930s could the pilot dispense with this natural aid to precise flying.

In general, engine instruments came before flight instruments, although aneroid barometers were soon adapted for aviation use by the simple process of translating the pressure reading into one of height: that was why early altimeters

map on the fixture mounted behind the front seat. Wires for pitch and roll control can be clearly seen attached to the control wheel yoke. Pilot and passenger are wearing purpose-designed flying clothing. (via Aeroplane Monthly)

Left *Handley Page Monoplane of 1911. The rpm indicator is driven by a flexible shaft from the engine; aneroid recording barometer on the foredeck as altimeter, oil and fuel pressure instruments; throttle and mixture levers on the control column and fuel tank pressurizing pump on the right.* (Smiths Industries)

had a pointer movement which was anti-clockwise for increasing height.

Early cockpits, therefore, usually had engine instruments if nothing else. In the early years engines were temperamental and unreliable, and so needed careful manipulation and continuous observation of their state of health. Airspeed was what you could coax from an engine which had a small range of rpm: it was either going flat out or it had stopped. Visual indication of oil pressure was provided by a glass bulb 'pulsometer' indicator mounted in view of the pilot.

When the BE2, the forerunner of the famous BE2c, was exhibited at the Olympia aviation exhibition in London before the First World War it was equipped with one of the first integrated panel of instruments. A tachometer, airspeed indicator, stop watch and altimeter were housed in a cast aluminium panel identified as the 'WD Mk. IV instrument board' produced by Elliott Brothers.

Part of the 'instrumentation' available to all pilots has always been the relationship between his aircraft and the visible

Casella MkIV integrated instrument panel of about 1912: height, airspeed and rpm. (Smiths Industries)

earth. In the early years and throughout the biplane years, bracing wires, tops of engine cowlings and other excrescences in the pilot's forward view provided cues relating to the progress of a take-off, landing or manoeuvre. With tail-wheeled aircraft, and unlike the later tricycle undercarriage machines, there was a correct attitude and speed for touching down, which had very little margin for error. Therefore a particular feature of the forward parts of an aircraft provided the datum for setting against the far side of the airfield.

It was not until 1912 that a scientific paper on the design of instruments specifically for aircraft was read. Up to that time reliance had been placed upon the direct use or adaptation of existing scientific instruments – such as the aneroid barometer for indicating height or the apparently unscientific length of string to indicate sideslipping. Even ten years after the Wright Brothers' pioneering flight the demand for flight instruments was not significant. Reasons for this include the preoccupation with aerodynamics, structures and controls as well as with the reliability of the available engines. There were more important things to worry about than instruments. If you got off the ground: good. The difference between take-off speed and cruising speed was small. Few aviators took to the air with the intention of claiming that 'I can go faster than you'. Even at aerial competitions, such as the great meeting at Reims in 1909, the winner was usually the one who got round the course without engine or structural failure. With most flights limited to fine weather with light winds, and with flight levels below any clouds, the pilot's instinctive sense of direction and of what was up and what was down was sufficient to keep control of his frail machine.

However, in the years immediately preceding 1914 the need for an accurate airspeed indicator was emphasized by the number of crashes resulting from trying to fly too slowly and then stalling.

Therefore the prudent aviator added an airspeed indicator to his inventory of barometer and rpm indicator. A typical early airspeed indicator had a flat plate, hinged and balanced by a spring or weight, so that the forward motion through the airstream provided an indication of speed as the flat plate was forced back by its drag. The 'flat plate' principle remained in use for many years as a standby airspeed indicator even though the pitot-head device, operating as a form of differential pressure instrument, was introduced to aviation as early as 1910. The earliest types of 'pitot' airspeed indicators were manometers. The differential air pressure from the pitot and static pipes being connected to the manometer glass tube: airspeed indication being shown by the height of the liquid. Within a short time the manometer type airspeed indicators were being replaced by a diaphragm mechanism with a pointer moving over a scale.

There was no particular reason why the airspeed indicator pointer should not have moved anti-clockwise for increasing speed; nevertheless the accepted stereotype from steam engineering was adopted – i.e. clockwise for increasing value, as with a pressure gauge.

Stalling, of course, was also the outcome of flying at an angle-of-attack outside the aircraft's design characteristics. Therefore among the first specifically aviation instruments to be developed was the vane type incidence (sic) indicator. Bubble-in-glass tube indicators were adapted as inclinometers to give the pilot some idea of pitch or roll angles. They were somewhat crude compared with later instruments, and except when the aircraft was in steady flight were subject to errors caused by rapid changes in aircraft attitude and heading and by acceleration.

The Admiralty in Britain was one of the earliest authorities to issue a minimum list of instruments for aircraft. Prior to the First World War the list specified: watch, longitudinal inclino-

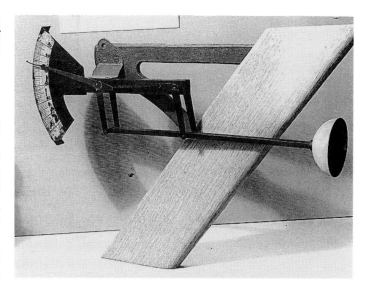

meter, side slip indicator (sic), airspeed indicator and electrical rpm indicator. By 1917 instrument lists were likely to be similar to that of the US Signal Corps which specified: altimeter, airspeed indicator, magnetic compass, air and oil pressure, tank contents, coolant temperature, tachometer and clock.

Drag cup airspeed indicator designed for strut mounting. (Smiths Industries)

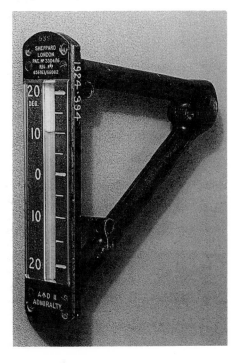

Admiralty inclinometer made by Sheppard of London. (Smiths Industries)

Instruments circa
1914: the early
aircraft compass,
inclinometer,
altimeter, pulsometer,
rpm of an Avro 504K.
(Smiths Industries)

Significantly these two lists, only four years apart, differ by the inclusion of an altimeter in the latter. The altimeter did not acquire its present listing as a primary and essential instrument until after the ten pioneering years of flight.

The mariner's magnetic compass was modified for use in aircraft, where it found a very different environment. On board a ship the compass was rarely subjected to a sudden and rapid precession of the vessel through many degrees of heading.

By the end of the First World War the total aviation experience of man and machine had been multiplied many times over. Thousands of aircraft had been produced and thousands of pilots, maintenance crews and design and production personnel had been exposed to this type of transport and fighting machine. The 'new technology' of aviation had established itself in just over fifteen years. During that time instruments had been either specially developed for aviation or had been adapted from other forms of transport, such as the road vehicle.

The demands of war had encouraged the more rapid development of practical instruments. Hitherto scientists had applied their knowledge to the problems, but the lack of suitable materials had often delayed the introduction of production standard instruments. Now Bourden tube mechanisms for pressure indicators, fabric or metal diaphragm mechanisms for altimeters and airspeed indicators, as well as remote indicating electrical indicators for rpm, were available. In 1917 Smiths Industries in the UK, for example, started production of the Clift oilskin diaphragm airspeed indicator.

To the early aviator clouds were as uncharted rocks to a mariner. They had to be avoided. Once in cloud the most skilful pilot could become confused by the apparent sensations of turning, attitude and other aircraft movement. Instruments by which the pilot could maintain steady flight in cloud were design goals which would occupy the aviation industry for the next 20 years.

The pilots

In the first ten years of aircraft development the majority of pilots were a combination of innovator and adventurer. Most had sufficient resources to enable them to pursue what was, at the time, and expensive occupation – or should one say, 'hobby'.

None of the pioneering pilots could be said to belong to a particular group of people: the skill of piloting an aircraft was yet to be defined and measured. However, within the first year of war there emerged a distinct group of people who as individuals exhibited a common set of characteristics: good reflexes and hand and eye co-ordination; and stamina to withstand the rigours of the open cockpit.

The air war imposed a standard method of training pilots and this in turn encouraged the development of a 'standard' pilot. From the first 'air experience' flight to being shot down, and more than likely killed, only a few weeks might elapse. Yet from this appalling waste of each nation's most intelligent and fit young men emerged a common pattern. The First World War pilot became a hero not only because of the aerial victories but because he ventured into the air. Most people could relate to the worlds of the soldier and sailor, but the 'air' was an unknown element to all but a few.

After the war, those pilots who had survived and then had the luck to find employment in civil aviation were still admired. By analogy with the captain of a ship, in the public mind the airline pilot acquired a degree of reverence.

Above *BE2 Experimental* circa 1913: pilot aft — protected by an early example of a vee-shaped windscreen — passenger or observer forward. On the nearest strut can be seen a pitot head as a sensor for a cockpit-mounted airspeed indicator. (via Aeroplane Monthly)

Right *Vickers Gunbus* circa 1915 (rebuilt in the 1970s): instruments not necessarily as in the original. (British Aerospace)

CHAPTER TWO

COCKPITS OF WAR

Biplanes and monoplanes

Britain's embryo flying service, the Naval and Military Wings of the Royal Flying Corps, possessed a number of different aircraft types prior to the outbreak of war in 1914. Among this variety of types were four basic design features: monoplanes, biplanes, tractor airscrews and pusher airscrews. Ailerons were superseding wing warping, and tail surfaces were superseding canards.

As the war progressed from the movement of armies to static trench warfare, the pioneering style of aviation was quickly superseded by aircraft types and operational practices which reflected the change from reconnaissance-only flights to fighting, bombing and ground attack. Cockpits, like aircraft, acquired functional shapes and equipment. With few instruments provided, the '1914' cockpit was uncluttered by much furniture and fittings. The most significant change came with the advent of the fixed forward-firing machine-guns which then took up some of the space.

The BE2c, of which over 1,000 were eventually supplied to the Royal Flying Corps, was not produced in great numbers until 1916. Yet its principal features set a standard for other types of aircraft. From the pilot's point of view the interplane gap of six feet and the small fuselage gave him and his observer a good view ahead, even with the latter in the front seat.

In an attempt to improve both the visibility and field of fire, the Royal Aircraft Factory at Farnborough schemed up the BE9. This had a cockpit for the observer and his Lewis gun mounted in front of the tractor propeller. The cockpit was carried on a bearing attached to the propeller boss. This out-in-front frail-looking cockpit was stabilized by wires running back, and clear of the propeller, to attachment points on the wings and undercarriage. At least, in the conventional tandem cockpits pilot and observer could communicate by shouting, arm signals and notes; in the BE9 they could only communicate by arm signals.

If the BE2c had any vices then, according to contemporary accounts, it was its stability. This made it easy to fly but very reluctant to indulge in the sort of manoeuvres necessary to avoid an enemy fighter. Later in the war the BE2c was modified as an anti-Zeppelin 'gunship'.

The Vickers FB5 Gunbus represented the RFC's only front-line fighter during the early part of the First World War. With the engine behind the pilot driving a pusher airscrew, and with the cockpit forward of the wings, the pilot had an excellent forward view. His view of hostile aircraft astern, though, was somewhat

Right *FE2, circa 1918: external to the bottom of the cockpit can be seen a venturi for suction-operated instruments and a propeller-driven electric generator either for a wireless installation or for illuminating the instruments. External to the rim of the pilot's cockpit is one of the bomb release levers.* (via Aeroplane Monthly)

Below *A side view of an FE2b showing the disposition of the two cockpits.* (via Aeroplane Monthly)

limited. However, the observer in the front cockpit, who operated the forward Lewis gun, could stand up and look back over the upper plane – and, presumably, shake a fist at any pursuers.

The FE2b of 1915 which followed the Gunbus into service eventually had a second Lewis gun for tail defence. This was mounted on a pillar so that the observer could stand up and face aft in his forward cockpit, and beat off attackers approaching from astern. A similar arrangement was eventually adopted for the Gunbus as a result of squadron experience.

With the propeller behind them, the pilots of the pushers were in a slightly less arduous environment than those who flew tractor rotaries, because the slipstream did not contain castor oil.

The FE2b had a distinctive cockpit outline, with the fuselage rising from shoulder level to above the pilot's head. Anticipating attack helicopter layouts of the 1970s, the FE2b cockpits were arranged with the forward one lower than the pilot's head so as to give an uninterrupted view ahead.

Pilots and observer-gunners were prevented from falling out of their cockpits by a broad lap strap. Camel pilots have recounted their experiences of flipping out of their lap strap when that 'mind of its own' machine tried to throw its rider. Oliver Sutton of the RFC made a notable contribution to pilot safety when he devised a four-strap harness with one securing pin. This Sutton harness could then be released from one central point where all the straps met.

The DH1 and DH2 single-seat pushers were specifically designed as fighters. The single forward-firing Lewis gun was on a swivel mounting; to fire the gun the pilot had to grip the butt and trigger. Should the right hand or the left be used for the gun? Apparently there was some controversy over the question of which hand

Principal elements of a Sopwith Camel. (Author)

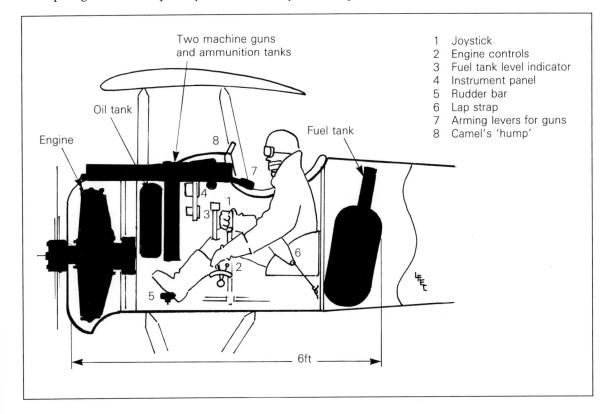

Two machine guns
and ammunition tanks

Oil tank

Engine

8

Fuel tank

6ft

1 Joystick
2 Engine controls
3 Fuel tank level indicator
4 Instrument panel
5 Rudder bar
6 Lap strap
7 Arming levers for guns
8 Camel's 'hump'

should be used for what, when flying and firing at the same time. Eventually it was realized that the pilot's task would be simplified if the gun were fixed so that the pilot just had to aim the aircraft.

By the middle of the First World War 'pusher' aircraft went out of fashion. This was a good thing for pilots and others who otherwise stood a good chance of being crushed by the engine in a crash. Even earlier, in 1914, the US Signal Corps had consigned all pusher types to the scrap heap. This decision followed numerous crashes in which the pilot had been fatally injured by the engine. This compared adversely with the number who survived crashes in 'tractor' aircraft.

Among the aircraft of the First World War, the Sopwith Camel provides an example of cockpit design, aircraft handling and pilot problems typical of fighter operations in Europe in the last two years of the war.

The Sopwith Camel will always be associated with the Royal Flying Corps, the fierce air battles of 1917 and the hazardous trench strafing sorties of the closing stages. Of all the rotary engine aircraft, the Sopwith Camel gained the greatest reputation, though this was hotly contested by Sopwith Pups and Triplanes. To the student and inexperienced pilot, the Camel was unforgiving if mishandled; to those who survived their initial frightening experience it became a formidable weapon, despite the violent changes of attitude following a change in engine speed and the strong gyroscopic coupling effect of the spinning mass of the rotary engine.

Camel interlude

The last winter of the First World War: dawn: an RFC Camel pilot returns the salute of his air mechanic. At such an early hour he could do without the mechanic's comments on the weather, even though well-intentioned.

Walking round his aircraft the pilot makes sure that all the bits that form this peculiar marriage of fabric, wires, wood and metal are in their rightful places and functioning correctly. He climbs aboard from the left side and feels the aircraft adjust its shape to his weight as he settles himself in the wickerwork seat. Some of the newer aircraft have metal seats.

'Switches off, Sir?' The pilot checks that the two magneto switches are in down 'off' position. 'Switches off.' The mechanic pulls the propeller round to draw the mixture of castor oil and petrol into the cylinders of the rotary engine. Mixture and throttle controls are set. The mechanic calls, 'Contact'. The pilot moves the switches to the up position and repeats, 'Contact'. The propeller is swung by the mechanic. Only a cough and a splutter. Try again. At the third attempt the engine 'catches'.

Just in front of the pilot's feet the rotary engine spins like an angry top as it drives itself and the propeller bolted to the crankcase around the stationary crankshaft.

The exhaust smoke from the engine includes castor oil. A contemporary account of the Camel's rotary engine mentions that 60 per cent of the lubricating oil went straight out of the exhaust valves – only the remainder being usefully employed. On this subject there appears to be some controversy over the possible ill-effects of inhaling castor oil laden exhaust fumes; the general opinion being that pilots' stomachs did suffer, but the evidence for this is not easy to trace.

Giving the crossed arms 'chocks away' signal, and with a burst of throttle to get the aircraft moving, the pilot taxies out to the downwind side of the airfield. A mechanic at each wing tip helps to control the aircraft, which is not easy to manoeuvre unaided when on the ground. The air mechanic at the left wing tip digs in his heels to form a pivot as the Camel is swung into wind. A glance astern to check that no other aircraft is about to land, and at maximum revs the Camel rocks across the rough field and soars into the air.

He joins up with the others in the patrol and they head east. Soon after reaching their patrol altitude the flight leader rocks his Camel from side to side to attract everyone's attention and then pulls up into a climbing right turn. Just in time, for above the roar of the engines the pilots can hear the faint sound of machine-gun fire. Our pilot also hears, and feels as if someone were beating his aircraft with a stick. In his haste to keep in formation he pulls the Camel up and round too tightly. The controls suddenly go slack. The aircraft flops over and starts to gyrate in its familiar after-a-stall spin.

As this is not the first time he has found himself in a spin, our pilot is not concerned with how to stop it but when. In the spin he is a difficult target. But in the few seconds of recovery he is a sitting target as he re-establishes normal flight and gets the rotary engine running smoothly again. Coming out too soon is risky. Too late and he will hit the ground. He survives. But many do not.

The Camel proved more than a handful for the pilot straight from flying school. Having to concentrate so much on handling the aircraft, there was little time left in which to use it as a weapon. Only those with extra ability, plus a lot of luck, survived long enough to gain sufficient experience with which to make the most of the aircraft as a weapon system. They then stood a reasonable chance of surviving in a dogfight by making the best of the control characteristics and flying to the limit of the machine's structural strength.

The rotary engine of the Camel affected both aircraft handling characteristics and cockpit equipment, as well as influencing the preferred airfield circuit direction and approach path to a landing. Control of a rotary engine required four items: ignition switch, fine adjustment, throttle and 'blip' switch. Later versions of the rotary engine had twin magnetos and therefore there were twin ignition switches.

The 'blip' switch enabled the engine ignition to be cut momentarily as a means of controlling power. It was not prudent to try to control the engine with the throttle, because for each throttle position

Camel 2F1: RNAS 'Zeppelin' fighter circa 1918: The armament consists of one Vickers to port firing through the propeller and one Lewis gun on the centre section. The Lewis gun was not on a Foster mounting, as used by the RFC, but was installed inverted so that the ammunition drum could be reached by the pilot in flight. However, the sharp-eyed reader will note that in this photograph the gun is the normal way up! A propeller-driven generator for instrument lighting can be seen on one of the aft centre section struts. (via Aeroplane Monthly)

Sopwith Snipe circa 1918. The two Vickers guns dominate the cockpit, with the compass between them. On the right of each gun is the arming lever. Lower left can be seen the separate ignition switches for the two magnetos. The control column is surmounted by the blip switch button for the rotary engine. Convenient to the pilot's thumbs are the two gun triggers. Instrument lighting is provided. (via Aeroplane Monthly)

there was an optimum fine adjustment lever setting. Failure to achieve the correct setting of the two levers quickly enough could result in engine failure. Hence, when manoeuvring with no height to spare, it was essential to use the 'blip' switch.

Fighter pilots Bridgeman and Stewert, who combined to write about their First World War flying experiences under the title *The Clouds Remember*, recalled the torque effects produced by the Camel's rotary engine when using the thumb 'blip' switch: 'There was the same quick lurch of the wings as the engine came on and off ...'.

The engine, guns, cockpit and fuel tank were set close together. In place of a straight handgrip on the stick, the Sopwith control column was of triangular shape at the top. Convenient to the pilot's right hand thumb was the 'blip' switch, and arranged for finger control were the gun triggers. Projecting towards the pilot from the top of the instrument panel were the two arming levers for the Vickers guns. Other prominent cockpit items of that time were the hand pumps for pressurizing the fuel tank and the hydraulic system of the gun synchroniz-

ing gear. A windscreen was provided to keep some of the slipstream off the pilot. On the Sopwith Pup the windscreen was of unusual shape: it was set immediately behind the single Vickers gun and had a padded surround on which the pilot could rest his head when sighting for attack.

The types of instrument and their number tended to vary from squadron to squadron. A typical single-seat fighter would be equipped with an altimeter, engine rpm indicator, air pressure gauge, airspeed indicator and compass as well as a pulsometer.

One item that the pilot of a Camel might have expected to find was a length of bungee cord, to relieve him of the continuous forward pressure required on the control column to counter the built-in tail heaviness. A moment of relaxation and up went the nose. If this was not checked and the aircraft fell over into an inverted spin, then the chance of recovery was slim. As recalled by ex-Camel pilots: 'It would quickly flick into a spin in right-hand turns if the speed was too low'. In 1918 a dual-seat trainer version was used for instruction in spin recovery and right-hand circuits. This may be another example of an aircraft characteristic which made pilots prefer a left-hand circuit.

Guns in the cockpit

The earliest armament of the RFC consisted of pistols and rifles. When machine-guns such as the Lewis and the Vickers were given purpose-built mountings they were kept within reach of the pilot so that he could change the drum of the Lewis or attend stoppages of both types of gun. The guns were very much a part of the cockpit furniture. Even the upper wing-mounted Lewis was usually on a rail (the Foster mounting for example) which curved down towards the pilot. The mounting could be unlocked and the gun pulled down to the reloading position, or elevated for shooting at an overhead target such as an airship.

An early anecdote concerns L.A. Strange, who was changing the ammunition drum of an overhead Lewis gun. The drum was jammed on the mounting peg, so he used both hands to try to free it, keeping control by gripping the stick between his knees. He lost control and the aircraft became inverted. Fortunately he was able to hang on by the gun, otherwise, as he had undone his safety strap, he would have fallen to his death.

Unlike the Camel, the SE5a had only one fixed, forward-firing, synchronized gun as standard armament. This feature simplified the cockpit equipment as there was only one gun breech and arming lever intruding into the pilot's space. With the Vickers gun on the left, all the instruments were disposed in the centre and to the right.

The compass of the SE5a, and that of other contemporary Royal Flying Corps and Royal Naval Air Service aircraft types, was housed in a 'binnacle' with prominent correction units on top and to each side. Compared with the Camel, the SE5a with an in-line engine did not have a 'blip' switch. The ring-shaped control column grip had just the two gun triggers, which could be pressed to fire either the Vickers or the upper wing-mounted Lewis.

Part of the SE5a's cockpit furniture was the Aldis collimated sight, which looked like a telescope but was not, and which at that stage of the war had become a standard cockpit feature in British aircraft.

The Vickers gun was within reach of the pilot, who in the event of a stoppage could reach over and clout it with a leather mallet. The mallet was an important item of cockpit equipment in many aircraft of the time.

The Spad, of which there were a number of variants, was to the French what the Camel was to the RFC. One squadron of the RFC was equipped with

Foster mounting for the Lewis gun on an Avro 504K. Both sets of sights are equipped with illuminated posts. The ring and wire which depend from the rail of the Foster mounting operated the catch which allowed the gun to be drawn back down the rail, either for firing upward at a target or when changing an ammunition drum. (IWM)

Right *The DH9A,
circa 1918, which
remained in service
with the RAF for over
a decade, had a
Vickers gun
installation similar to
that in the SE5. The
pilot was provided
with both a ring and
bead sight and an
Aldis collimated (but
not telescopic) sight.
This is a good
example of 'the gun in
the cockpit' design
necessitated by the
unreliability of guns.*
(via Aeroplane
Monthly)

Below *Pilot and
gunner close together
— the Bristol Fighter,
circa 1917.*

Spads, and the design of the cockpit and its location produced some adverse comments from British evaluation pilots. They commented on the restricted view from the cockpit, which was hemmed in by the interplane structure and bracing wires, and they also criticized the gap between the upper plane and the fuselage decking over the engine and guns as being too narrow. With an in-line engine (a Hispano Suiza V8), there was no room for a fuel tank between pilot and engine — the rudder bar being immediately behind the engine crankcase. The fuel tank was in the wing centre section with a faired group of pipes descending to the engine and further marring the pilot's forward line of vision.

The two machine-guns (Vickers 7.7-mm) were staggered, with the right-hand gun forward of the left, and the RFC evaluation report included a reference to the difficulties a pilot had when trying to clear a stoppage in one of the guns. This is another example of a standard design feature of the biplane era, dictated by the unreliability of machine-guns, which therefore had to be placed within reach of the pilot. In other respects the Spad cockpit was typical of its time. But as there was only one RFC squadron with Spads it is unlikely that the throttle movement was altered from the French pull-to-open to the RFC's preferred push-to-open action.

The Bristol Fighter of 1917 was designed as a reconnaissance aircraft with the conventional pilot and observer cockpit arrangement. Eventually it was to perform nearly every role in the RFC and the RAF. With the pilot and observer-gunner within shouting distance of each other, the Bristol Fighter proved to be a formidable dogfighter, particularly when used in a formation of two or more aircraft. Weighing in at nearly twice the weight of a Camel, the 'Brisfit' was of sturdy construction, with a distinctive

Sopwith Snipe circa 1918. The centre section has been cut out to improve the pilot's upward view; twin Vickers guns in the hump as in the Camel.

step down in the upper profile at the pilot's cockpit. A small windscreen and sights were set on top of the very long forward fuselage and engine cowling. As usual the single forward Vickers gun projected back into the cockpit, where it was within reach of the pilot's assortment of 'persuading' tools should it jam.

In the closing stages of the war the Sopwith Snipe incorporated the experience gained from the production and operational use of the Camel, Pup and Triplane. With the intention of operating at – for those days – extreme altitudes, the pilot was provided with an electrically-heated flying suit and an oxygen system to keep him warm and alert at 20,000 feet. The cockpit was at the highest point of the hump-decked fuselage, so that even with the tail of the aircraft on the ground, the pilot could see directly ahead over the top of the engine cowling.

Wings back-staggered to improve the pilot's view, the Sopwith Hippo shared this arrangement with the Sopwith Dolphin and DH5. (via Aeroplane Monthly)

The problem of the restricted forward view from the cockpits of so many biplanes of the First World War encouraged some designers to use back-stagger; i.e. the upper plane was set back from the lower instead of the customary more forward position. The DH5 and Sopwith Dolphin were important examples. In the Dolphin the pilot was hemmed in by the engine and two Vickers guns in front and the fuel tank behind and by two Lewis guns mounted on a cross-tube in front of his head.

A fundamental characteristic of the majority of aircraft types from 1903 onwards has been symmetry in plan. However, cockpits and principal pilots have not always been on the centre line. The Wright Flyer had the pilot's position to the left of centre, with the engine to the right. Throughout the history of aviation there have been other asymmetrical aircraft. The pilot's position in the majority of cockpits has been to the left if, for some reason, it has not been possible to set it on the centre line. In aircraft with a fuselage wide enough to seat two crew members side-by-side the RAF, as will be explained, started out with the pilot or principal pilot in the right-hand seat.

Human hand and side preferences have

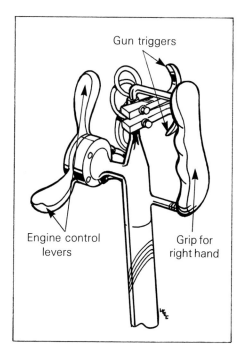

Gun triggers

Engine control
levers

Grip for
right hand

had some influence on the design of aircraft cockpits from the beginning of powered flight. Essentially this comes from the statistical fact that the majority of pilots are right-handed as well as preferring to use the right eye for aiming. The right-handed pilots preferred to hold the control requiring the greater sensitivity of touch in their right hand, but this is not to suggest that left-handed pilots are incapable of adapting to the common 'left hand on throttle, right hand on stick' layouts. Hence single-engined aircraft cockpits have usually had the throttle on the left. Yet the 'heavy' bombers of the First World War, such as the Handley Page 0/400 and V/1500, and the Vickers Vimy, had the pilot's position to the right, with the throttles and other engine controls on the pilot's right.

Keep to the right

Obviously, in the first decade of powered flight, rules of the road, such as to which side one should pass an opposing aircraft, were unnecessary because the chances of meeting another aircraft flying on an op-posite course were small.

In 1909 the Commission Aerienne Mixte promulgated rules which included: 'Keep to the right meeting' and 'At night display red, green and white lights as at sea'. In the same year important competitive events took place at Reims. The around-the-pylons course was arranged for both clockwise and anti-clockwise circuits. As it happened, the wind direction across the starting line required an anti-clockwise circuit, with the aircraft banking to the left around each pylon. The experience gained may have influenced subsequent circuits, the majority of which from 1909 onwards were flown anti-clockwise.

The torque and gyroscopic effects experienced by pilots of rotary engine aircraft prior to 1920 may also have encouraged the adoption of the left-hand circuit. This and the keep right rules combined to influence the design of the pilot's place and aviation practices down to this day.

However there is no clear connection between early British multi-engine aircraft cockpits and these rules and customs. The Handley Page 'big' bombers, the 0400 and the V1500, the Felixstowe flying boats and the Vickers Vimy, were given 'right-hand drive' open cockpits.

The obvious question to be answered is: 'Why was the principal pilot in British multi-engine machines seated on the right?' One answer is to be found in the fact that it was the RNAS which first specified and operated these aircraft and therefore the naval tradition that things, people and positions to starboard take precedence over those to port dominated the design. All this was before airway rules were introduced. Another origin may have been the automobile, the majority of which in all countries prior to about 1925 had right-hand drive.

The German flying services adopted an opposite arrangement and seated the only or principal pilot on the left. The Gotha V twin-engine bomber is an example. But

Junkers D1 — an early example (circa 1918) of HOTAS (hands on throttle and stick). (Author)

in one respect British and German practice was in concert. This was the positioning of the engine controls on the side of the pilot away from the gangway and therefore safe from inadvertent operation by a crew member passing to the forward position.

In relation to multi-engine types the German 'left-hand' arrangement was the familiar right hand on stick, left on throttle; whereas British pilots flew right hand on throttle in the multi-engine types. The British preference for seating the principal pilot on the right lingered on in both civil and RAF 'big' aircraft until about 1930. An example of a transport, albeit RAF but essentially civil in its use, is the Vickers Valentia, which was right-hand drive as late as 1941.

In the first version of the Fokker FIII of 1922 the pilot's place was on the right alongside the engine. In a later version of the FIII the pilot sat on the left of the engine so as to comply with airway rules. Sitting on the left the pilot was in the better position from which to observe

navigational landmarks when keeping to the right of an airway.

Subsequent civil aircraft development tended towards two pilots sharing a central controls pedestal. This also swept away many of the side preferences and practices, because pilots had to get used to either piloting from the left- or the right-hand seat and therefore operating the primary controls with either hand when adjusting the engine controls on a central pedestal.

In British cockpits 'port' and starboard' eventually achieved equal status with 'left' and 'right'. Although the RFC was part of the Army, 'nearside' and 'offside', as used for horses and vehicles, did not come into use. All this despite the preference for 'climbing aboard' or 'mounting' an aircraft from its left or nearside.

When the turn and slip indicator, for example, came into squadron use in the RAF, its dial was marked L and R, not P and S. However, ignition switch pairs were usually marked Port and Starboard. Eventually steering orders to a pilot from

It's anti-clockwise round the pylons for this circuit at an Edwardian aviation meeting at Hendon.

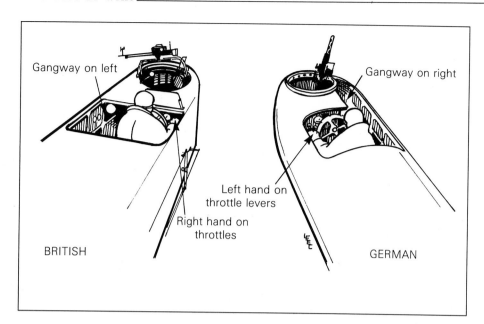

Gangway on left

Gangway on right

Left hand on
throttle levers

Right hand on
throttles

BRITISH

GERMAN

*Comparison between
British and German
cockpit arrangements,
circa 1917.* (Author)

the bomb-aimer were given as 'right' or 'left-left', even though the bomb sight and navigational aids were marked Port and Starboard.

'Port' and 'starboard' serves to introduce First World War flying boat cockpits. A good example is the Felixstowe F and H series of twin-engined biplane flying boats, derived from the Curtiss and Porte designs. These graceful-hulled aircraft provided the main RNAS coastal and North Sea patrol force from 1914 to 1918, and improved versions remained with the RAF until the late 1920s.

The principal pilot of a Felixstowe sat in the right-hand seat of the main cockpit with only a small sports car size windscreen. The H12 version of 1917 had an enclosed pilot's cockpit. This was innovative: few other aircraft types had this feature, which was a considerable concession to crew comfort.

The cockpit furnishings of a Felixstowe flying boat included an instrument panel in front of the captain, but there were no instruments in front of the second pilot, who sat with his legs in the hatchway to the open bow cockpit, which the front gunner shared with the

anchor cable windlass. The engine tachometers, directly driven by flexible shafts from the engines, were mounted with one on the left side and the other on the right side of the cockpit. In those years there was only limited supervision of the numerous modifications made by a squadron. Therefore because of the number of variations among the different H12s and F boats it is not possible to say which had a 'standard' cockpit, controls and instruments.

Not surprisingly, in those times the aileron control wheels were of substantial diameter. With numerous lengths of control cable passing through a number of pulleys, and with flexing of the structure, the control system tended to be sloppy.

These first-generation flying boats were extremely tiring to fly. At the end of an eight-hour patrol in an H12, without dual control and no easy access to the cockpit, the pilot was at the limit of his physical endurance.

Photographs of British First World War pilots and aircrew often include wearers of 'fug boots' — thigh length fleece-lined boots. These were essential items of clothing for the crew of an F2.

A 1918 advertisement for the Burberry

The cockpit of a Felixstowe F flying boat. Principal pilot's position on the right; control wires in full view; opening forward to the bow gun and mooring position; anchor windlass forward of the instrument panel. (Crown Copyright)

Carapace Airsuit or 'Sheath Armour for Knights of the Air' includes the following: 'The Carapace Airsuit is made of three layers, each of different material, scientifically combined so as to give the greatest resistance against wet and cold. The outer covering is of the famous weatherproof Burberry Gabardine, so densely woven and proofed that it will withstand intense pressure from wind or rain. Next comes a luxurious interlining of woollen fleece giving maximum warmth with minimum weight. The innermost lining is of glissade, which enables the airman to slip into the suit without a moment's delay or trouble.'

British and German 'heavies'

A right-hand drive, one-pilot cockpit, open to the elements, came as no shock to a pilot posted to a Handley Page 0/400 squadron. Other aircraft of the time gave the pilot no better protection. In some respects, as the cockpit was ahead of the propellers, the rush of air at 100 mph was more bearable than in a single-engined machine.

Only the essential flight instruments, altimeter, airspeed indicator, clock, inclinometer and compass were mounted within the cockpit, along with the primary controls and the throttle control, magneto switches, starting magneto, light and bomb selector switches. All the engine instruments (temperature, oil pressure, rpm) were on the inboard side of each engine nacelle. This arrangement certainly simplified the instrument systems but at the same time emphasized the good eyesight requirement for pilots.

The 0/400 exhibited an early example of what we now term ergonomic design, i.e. the relationship between man and machine was taken into account. In place of individual throttle levers there was a single lever moving in the expected direction, which was forward for more thrust. This controlled the throttles of both engines simultaneously. To open or close the throttle of one engine relative to the other there was a flat knob on top of the lever. Turning this anti-clockwise increased the starboard engine and decreased the port and vice versa.

The heavy bomber squadrons of the RNAS and later the RAF operated at freezing altitudes, around minus 4°C at 10,000 feet, making life in open cockpits unbearable, particularly on a long-range operation. Eventually the crews of the 0/400s were given electrically heated flying clothing.

The heated flying clothing, instruments, electrical systems, two engines and all-up weights of five tons appear, 70 years or more later, to be the only surviving representatives of an archaic technology. Yet to those who flew for the RAF in 1918, only 15 years after the success of the Wright Flyer of 1903, the advance in technology must have seemed absolutely outstanding.

Contemporary German bombers, such as the Gotha V, were, in many respects, better equipped. For example, by 1918 oxygen was available to the crew. In comparison, oxygen was not provided for the crews of the RAF's HP 0400s and, so it appears, was not specified for the V1500s: albeit these aircraft had an effective maximum operating height of around 10,000 feet. However it was considered for the DH4s and DH9s used for daylight raids so that they could keep well above German fighters. Some of these were equipped with oxygen as well as an electrical supply for heated flying clothing. Had the First World War not ended when it did, it is likely that the majority of aircraft on both sides would have had oxygen systems as standard and their crews electrically-heated clothing for operations above 15,000 feet.

One important technical advance by 1918 was 'in the cockpit' radio equipment. However, radio communication in both the British and French air services was limited in general to reconnaissance and artillery-spotting aircraft. It was not fully developed for fighter aircraft until 1918. The Royal Flying Corps, for ex-

ample, tried out radio-telephony (RT) from 1916 onwards. It is interesting to note that the experiments emphasized the need for close-fitting helmets for the pilots because of the low power of the received signals. The comparatively low frequency used required long trailing aerials. Until pilots always remembered to 'wind-in' before landing, many aerial wires were left across roofs, trees and gardens adjacent to the airfield.

The German air services also developed ground-to-air radio communication. At the outbreak of war in 1914 there were over 30 wireless transmitters covering the German frontier and coastline. They also introduced early in the war strut-mounted, propeller-driven generators to supply power for an aircraft's radio equipment.

By way of a tube, oxygen could be inhaled by the crew of the Gotha V (this is a Vc), although what with the intense cold at high altitude, schnapps might have been just as welcome! Note the German preference for 'left-hand drive'. (Alex Imrie)

Two engines pulling and two pushing meant this formidable array of ignition switches for the captain of a Handley Page V 1500 — eight pairs, and eight mixture control levers for the eight carburettors alongside the pilot's right thigh. 'Right-hand drive'. (Smiths Industries)

The Handley Page V/1500 was conceived before the end of the war but was introduced into squadron service too late to bomb Berlin from 166 Squadron's home station of Bircham Newton. For its time, it was one of the 'heavies'. With four engines, two 'pulling' and two 'pushing', the V/1500 was both large and complex in comparison with other RAF aircraft; it even had a flight engineer's station. In the open cockpit, which was right-hand drive like the Handley Page 0/400 and the Vickers Vimy, there was an array of switches and levers for the four engines: a battery of eight double ignition switches, four throttles and four mixture controls. All these had to be fitted into the cubby-hole on the right of the cockpit which was the captain's position.

Typical of its time was the large control wheel, through which the pilot operated the ailerons via numerous cranks, pulleys and lengths of cable. The control wheel had to have a diameter ap-proaching two feet and a 2:1 gear ratio to make the vast ailerons manageable. The control column could be locked in position to give the pilot a rest on long missions: a very primitive autopilot!

In anticipation of long-range operations across the Rhine in 1918, the RAF had developed a three-beacon radio position system to help the pilot navigators of this early example of a strategic air force.

The Vimy cockpit is worth looking at in some detail because it was typical not only of design practices of the last two years of the First World War but was, in general if not in particular, representative of the cockpits of many British transport aircraft of the ten years which followed.

The pilot sat on the right, with the co-pilot/navigator, wireless operator/mechanic squeezed in on the left. The functions and title of the second occupant depended on the type of operation being undertaken.

Above the pilot's feet and below the small instrument panel was the main fuel

The noise from the four engines of the Staaken Riese bomber, circa 1917, was so great that the crew members could only communicate using electrically operated panels at each position. Perhaps the most important feature is the fully enclosed 'flight deck'. (Alex Imrie)

Looking back from the front gunner's cockpit of a Staaken Riese. (Alex Imrie)

The wire guards aside the Vimy bomber-transport, circa 1919, are to stop pilots getting their arms too close to the propellers. The engine nacelle-mounted instruments are to be seen, and one of the earlier examples of a fairing behind the pilot's head. (Vickers)

Vimy cockpit: large aileron wheel; combined throttle for the two engines (lower right); four separate ignition switches with starter magneto to the left; fuel tank selector controls and 'plumbing' as well as hand pump in front of the pilot. The switch on the left is typical and little different from an ornate domestic light switch. (Science Museum)

system control panel. This included the fuel pressure indicator, main fuel cock levers, as well as the wobble pump used when transferring fuel from one tank to another.

The rudder bar was just that: a bar to which the fully exposed and duplicated rudder cables were directly connected. Incidentally, no provision was made for adjusting the rudder bar to match a pilot's leg length; in this respect the Vimy was no different from the majority of contemporary aircraft types. Also exposed were the aileron control cable and chain which passed over a sprocket wheel at the top of the control column. The wheel itself would not have looked out of place in the cockpit of a 1920 sports car. Of course, the particular Vimy to which these comments refer is the Alcock and Brown 'Transatlantic' machine, now resting in the Science Museum, London. In those early years of air transport there was little standardization of instruments and controls, so this particular aircraft may not

be representative of Vimys in general. The same caveat must apply to other aircraft types.

As an example of the dangers of arguing from the particular to the general: the ignition switches in the Science Museum Vimy are arranged as separate units for each of the four magneto systems and not, as became more general, paired switches for each engine.

Alcock and Brown's eastbound flight across the Atlantic in their Vimy in June 1919 required considerable stamina, fortitude and resourcefulness. They were beset by extremes of weather, including fog as well as icing. Occasionally one of them had to climb out of the open cockpit and work his way out to each of the engines in turn in order to scrape the ice off the engine instruments so that they could be read from the cockpit. It would be some years before aircraft designers abandoned nacelle-mounted instruments in favour of the more expensive and complicated cockpit instruments, thereby af-

A typical example of instruments, armament and controls in a fighter aircraft of the 1920s — the cockpit of the Martinsyde ADC1. Apart from the cross level inclinometer, instruments to enable flight to proceed without sight of the horizon are still awaited. (via Aeroplane Monthly)

fording an improvement in cockpit ergonomics.

The end of the First World War was not marked by a sudden and revolutionary change in cockpits. The 1918 generation of fighters, for example, were similar to those which had gone before. Of course, details had been improved, but essentially the cockpit and its equipment remained much as it had been in the preceding three years. Outwardly, however, a notable difference was the incorporation of a fairing behind the pilot's head in a number of single-seat aircraft types. In general, cockpits remained open with small windscreens, and guns continued to take up some of the pilot's

place. Seats were still of lightweight construction and shaped very much as they had been in the Bleriot monoplanes. The broad lap strap was being replaced by the more effective Sutton harness.

Inside the cockpit the number of instruments had increased during the last two years of the war. In some aircraft, the instruments were illuminated for night flying.

Perhaps the most important change to the military cockpit from about 1918 onwards was the general provision of parachutes. Before 1918 the German air services were the only users of parachutes.

CHAPTER THREE

COCKPITS BETWEEN THE WARS

Civil transports

In the years immediately after 1918 there were few incentives for improving the design of cockpits and their equipment.

When the war ended in November 1918 each of the major belligerent countries had accumulated thousands of aircraft. These were now superfluous to a peacetime economy. The embryo airlines of the immediate post-war era adapted military aircraft, with few modifications other than the removal of armament, to meet the needs of air transport. The cockpits which had been so familiar to hundreds of air force pilots became the cockpits of peace: albeit localized wars involving aviation occurred from time to time.

Inevitably, the abundant supply of aircraft among the victorious nations tended towards stagnation of design. Only when it was realized from practical experience that the key to successful air transport was adherence to a schedule was money devoted to improving the design of aircraft and of their cockpits.

In the 1920s passenger air transport began to evolve, particularly in the USA, Germany, France and Britain. After 1918 French aviation interests pushed ahead with civil air transport as fast as the available technology would allow.

A pioneer French air transport was the Farman Goliath of 1919 used on the Paris–London service. It afforded the passengers in the front row of seats an uninterrupted view ahead. The pilot and mechanic sat in an open cockpit under the leading edge of the upper wing. One item of cockpit equipment was very different in operation from its equivalent in the civil aircraft of the competing British airlines: this was the throttle lever for each engine. Until about 1945 the throttles in French and Italian aircraft were arranged so that to increase power the pilot pulled the levers back. Also in contrast to British practice the pilot sat on the left. Incidentally, this side preference required the passenger door to be on the right, because that was the side unobstructed by the elevator control cables.

Had fully enclosed cockpits been provided, these would have made it difficult for a pilot to navigate by reference to features on the ground — to towns, railway lines and roads, coastline, lakes and rivers. Without radio aids to navigation, the pilot's absolute dependence on flying by reference to the ground in order to verify his navigational calculations makes the American definition 'contact flying' most apposite.

German civil aviation, despite the post-war problems of the nation as a whole, developed rapidly. As with other coun-

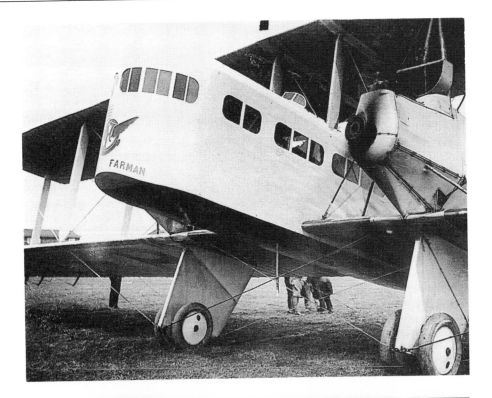

Atop the Farman Goliath, used on the pioneering Paris–London flights of 1919, is the windscreen of its open-top cockpit. (John Stroud)

The Farman Goliath's cabin interior — the pilot's position on a raised platform set among the passenger seats, with a gangway to the right. (John Stroud)

tries, the lessons of military aviation were applied to the design of transport aircraft and to airfield and navigational equipment. In one respect the German air services of the war years were very much in advance of others. This was in the provision of lighting systems for night flying. Considerable research had gone into the problems of night flying. Navigational lighthouses had been erected throughout Germany and horizontal illuminated panels had been developed to provide pilots with information on the state of an airfield and the wind strength and direction. This particular line of development provided Germany with a useful basis for starting up its civil aviation network after the war.

Flying the mail

The pioneering US Air Mail Service of the early 1920s not only highlighted the problems and deficiencies of aviation, it laid the foundation for efficient and safer

civil air transport in the future.

The air mail routes traversing the USA crossed areas of contrasting topography and weather conditions. The 'Hell Stretch', for example, across the Allegheny Mountains provided more problems than, say, crossing the clearly defined peaks of the Rockies. The Alleghenys were of the rolling hump-backed type. These forested mountains and valleys looked deceptively benign. Flying 'contact' above the confusing meanders of the mountain ridges a pilot could easily and quickly become lost; particularly when there was fog or the wind and visibility made sudden changes. Above all, and unlike other parts of the early mail routes, there were few clearings for use in an emergency among the miles and miles of tree-clustered slopes. On average one pilot was killed each month — usually in a DH4 biplane.

The DH4 of the RFC was also built under licence in the USA. It was modified for US Mail service by moving the pilot's

At the controls of the Fokker-Grulich F II used on Lufthansa routes in the early 1920s, the pilot-chauffeur sits in an open cockpit in front of the passenger compartment windscreen — an arrangement borrowed from contemporary motor car design. (John Stroud)

position to the aft cockpit: the forward cockpit then became the mail hold. Apart from avoiding large changes of trim with different payloads, the aft cockpit provided more protection for the pilot in the event of a crash — a not unusual event in those early years of commercial flight.

By 1923 the 'airmail' DH4s were fitted with electric landing lights, landing flares and flame dampers on the exhaust pipes to improve their night flying potential. The night sector between Chicago and Cheyenne, which had fewer areas of high ground than other sectors, was marked by 18-inch rotating beacons at each of the emergency landing strips set out 25 miles apart. At three-mile intervals there were smaller flashing beacons. The major airfields displayed 36-inch rotating beacons on 50-foot towers. These were visible on a clear night for over 100 miles. Unfortunately this otherwise excellent array of navigational aids was of little use in poor visibility.

Without adequate 'blind' flying instruments a pilot caught in a snowstorm had to risk descending in order to fly 'contact' and find a suitable spot on which to land. Otherwise he could be forced to take to the parachute — something which Lindbergh had to do on two occasions as an airmail pilot.

Before the installation of electric or gas 'lighthouses' to mark the route, large bonfires were lit once the telephone message giving the expected time of arrival was received.

Contributing to the hazards of flying the mail planes was the lack of an adequate weather information service. The mail pilots needed both actual and forecast weather — particularly visibility. Eventually radio receivers, even at 150 pounds in weight, were introduced, and served to improve both the safety and regularity of the service.

Airmanship

Many 'airliners' in the 1920s and even sometimes in the 30s, only reached their

destination through the 'airmanship' of the pilot who, having picked out a landmark, such as the Eiffel Tower rising above a sea of cloud, was able to make a carefully timed pattern and descent until he 'smelt' the grass of the airfield. In a completely enclosed cockpit this type of flying was more difficult.

In 1919, the operations of one of the earliest UK schedule operators, Air Transport & Travel (AT&T), were distinguished by the painting of the name on the roofs of railway stations at Redhill, Tonbridge, Ashford and Edenbridge which lay on the conveniently straight course of the South Eastern and Chatham Railway towards Dover. This easily distinguishable railway track provided a most convenient navigational aid on the way to Paris. In the event of engine failure the pilot could look for one of the emergency landing grounds which were spaced about every 20 miles. Should an engine fail or the visibility begin to deteriorate, the pilot was better able to pick out an emergency landing ground when seated in an open cockpit.

The open cockpit was also retained well into the 1930s because of the difficulties of keeping the windscreen clear of rain and ice.

As late as 1930, to quote from a contemporary report, the Westland Wessex tri-motor had 'sliding windows at the side of the cockpit giving a good view ... the fact that they can be opened enables the pilot to put his head outside during a landing ...'. Like many pre-1945 cars, the forward cockpit window could be hinged up to give a clear view. At this time windscreen wipers and heated glass had not been developed as reliable production items.

Pilot safety

In 1919 the RAF, as an example of one of the world's principal air forces, was being reduced to a shadow of its former size, and was fighting for its existence as an independent service. For the time being it

Above *A car-type hinged windscreen as fitted to the Westland Wessex, circa 1929, to enable flight to continue in rain or snow.* (via Aeroplane Monthly)

Left *Wearing an Irvin seat type parachute, the pilot of an Armstrong Whitworth Atlas, circa 1930, of an RAF university air squadron.* (via Aeroplane Monthly)

had to make do with what it had.

Available resources of the RAF and industry were applied to eliminating structural failures and to improving engine reliability and performance. Improvements to cockpit equipment and to pilot comfort tended to be given a low priority. Eventually, though, pilot safety was given attention and in October 1919 Calthrop parachutes were issued to the crews of Avro 504Ks. Other aircraft types followed and by 1924 the RAF had standardized the Irvin parachute for the majority of aircraft crews. In the USA the Irvin parachute was already in use.

In contrast to the extreme design variations of the first half of World War One, cockpits were now expected to be positioned just abaft or under the upper wing in single-engined aircraft. Pushers and unusual cockpit locations were consigned to the archives.

For five years after the war the RAF marked time. Eventually it received new aircraft: Woodcock, Siskin, Grebe and Gamecock are representative of the fighters of the 1920s. All had open cockpits and synchronized fuselage-mounted guns placed within reach of the pilot. In the Gamecock the pilot sat with his head just below the trailing edge of the centre section.

The designer of a fighter cockpit in the Twenties and Thirties had to resolve two basic and conflicting requirements: one, positioning the equipment in such a way as to simplify the pilot's many tasks; and two, simplifying the mechanical linkages which connected cockpit controls to the different aircraft systems and equipment, such as throttle and mixture levers to the engine, fuel tank pressurizing pump handle to pump, and so on.

In the end, practical considerations usually dictated a compromise. The primary controls, obviously, had to be within reach of the pilot's hands and feet but many other controls, such as wheels, levers and cocks were sometimes awkwardly positioned; otherwise their control linkages would have been unduly complex and expensive. Electrical controls gave the designer greater freedom of choice because wires could be laid round, over and across other items. Regrettably, though, even switches were sometimes figuratively 'thrown in' to land where they might.

The pilot's cockpit of the Vickers Vixen 'military two-seater', a tandem two-seat multi-role combat aircraft circa 1923. Above the white triangle of the fuel selector panel can be seen the row of rate-of-turn lights on a Reid Control Indicator. Forward of the windscreen are two transparent panels (port holes) which pass daylight onto the instrument panel. (Vickers)

Hawker Hart front cockpit circa 1930, which can be regarded as representative of inter-war RAF cockpits in general. The recently introduced Reid and Sigrist turn and bank indicator occupied a prominent position on the instrument panel. The ignition switches are still of the domestic brass domed type on a ceramic base. A feature of cockpits which would remain for at least another decade are the exposed 'bilges', into which loose objects and mud would collect until the next inverted flight released them. The simple sector plate with indicator 'bug' below the inclinometer shows the degree to which the radiator has been extended into the slipstream. (via Aeroplane Monthly)

On the subject of switches, the majority of designers adopted the practice early on of DOWN for ignition OFF, and UP for ignition ON, which was in conflict with domestic practice. The reason for this apparent anomaly, which is still the standard, is the principle that in the down/off position the self-contained magneto ignition system is 'earthed' ('grounded') out and therefore safe.

An unusual piece of detective work was needed to determine the cause of a number of crashes at an RAF gunnery school in the late 1920s. Pilots dived their aircraft at a ground target. As they pulled out from the attack the engine would stop. Not until an investigating pilot repeated the dive attacks and by chance glanced at the ignition switches during the pull-out was it realized that the heavy brass 'domestic' switches were being moved to the 'off', i.e. down, position by the positive G effect.

Until the forties the 'bilges' were in full view beneath the pilot's seat and ready to trap any dropped objects. Rubbish of all kinds remained below until negative G was applied, when a shower of odds and ends, including dried mud, fell past the pilot's head. Included in the contents of the bilges might be a screwdriver or spanner.

Despite discipline and high standards of aircraft maintenance, numerous incidents and, regrettably, accidents were caused by loose objects falling into control wires, rods, levers and pulleys — not to mention spilt liquids from thermos flask and cup getting into electrical apparatus.

Occasionally an unyielding object would lodge in a control linkage, thereby limiting its movement or completely jamming it in one position. Since the earliest days a primary pre-flight drill has been to check that the controls are free and are responding correctly to the movement of stick and rudder bar. Yet the history of aviation includes many disasters caused by incorrectly rigged controls.

Despite the care and attention lavished on the Short Crusader seaplane entered for the Schneider Trophy contest at Venice in September 1927 it crashed on take-off. Fortunately the pilot was rescued. The cause: the aileron controls had been crossed. As the aircraft lifted off the water, presumably the pilot anticipated the strong torque reaction of the propeller, which caused the aircraft to roll to the left, and applied right bank, with unfortunate consequences.

Even after 40 years of aviation there were numerous examples of controls being incorrectly rigged and subsequently not spotted during the pre-flight checks. In 1947 a prototype British airliner, the Tudor, and its chief designer, Roy Chadwick, were lost through crossed controls.

Throughout the assembly of the prototype Tudor the customary checks and double checks were made on all the controls. Nevertheless after all the inspection procedures had been completed it was found necessary, at the last minute, to disconnect the aileron controls. On reconnecting the wires they were crossed. In the cockpit, the test pilot carried out the pre-flight check that the controls moved freely. But he did not, or could not, verify that when he moved the wheel anticlockwise the left aileron moved up and the right one moved down to effect a left bank.

Soon after take-off the Tudor banked to one side. The bank became steeper until the aircraft crashed.

More open cockpits

Why was the open cockpit retained for fighter and two-seat air force aircraft until the mid-1930s? Among a number of reasons, two were that with some aircraft there was the danger of fumes from the engine, and pilots liked to feel the wind on their face because it was a useful indication of the aircraft's response to the controls; and perhaps a third was to be found in the outdoor pursuits of those pilots who drove 'open cockpit' sports cars or sailed when it was not 'done' to put up the hood or seek protection from the elements. Were the pilots of the twenties and the thirties like Victorian engine

'Cruising down the river'... the Short Calcutta — open cockpit, mooring hatch forward — typical of its kind. (Shorts)

Winston Churchill and Oswald Short, with Lankester Parker in front, in the cockpit of a Short Calcutta flying boat, circa 1929, before the aircraft was handed over to Imperial Airways. (Shorts)

drivers who resented the suggestion that they were not robust enough to brave cold, wind and rain and therefore should be enclosed by a cab?

We have come to accept the principle that fighter pilots are directed by ground control to a favourable tactical position. But we may forget that in the twenties and thirties, little different from 1918, a pilot needed a good all-round view when searching for the enemy. He did not want the structural members of an enclosed cockpit adding to the forest of interplane struts and rigging wires. In the days before R/T between aircraft, communication depended on arm and hand signals: impracticable from an enclosed cockpit. In the RAF, arm signals were referred to as 'zogging'.

With the Boeing P-12 biplane US Navy fighter of 1928 the pilot could trim it to fly 'hands off' and then, as one pilot explained: 'Poke your left hand out. She'll do a nice turn to the left'.

Flying boats too had open cockpits.

Little protection was given to the crew against waves breaking over the bow or spray picked up by the propellers and blown forward when taxying downwind.

Owners and pilots

As commercial flying expanded and as aircraft became larger and faster, so the social standing of the pilot rose in the eyes of the general public. But it was something that few pilots gave much thought to: their main concern during the 1920s and 30s, when not concentrating on flying, was generally the size of their pay packet.

It is a fact of civil aviation life that in the twenties, and to some extent in the thirties, few airline executives had much respect for their pilots. A common attitude was a mixture of 'They behave as if this were still on the Western front' and 'After all they are only drivers'. This attitude was not hard to find, and the history of Hillman's Airways records that

Edward Hillman saw virtually no difference in skill or status between his pilots and the drivers of his large fleet of buses. Hillman harboured none of the popular and romantic ideas about the experience, skill and initiative needed by pilots. To him a pilot was merely a driver and was treated as such.

Even the sometimes august captains and co-pilots of Imperial Airways were subject to petty actions by management. For example, the steward was not allowed to serve them any refreshments.

The gulf between management and pilots was matched by the distance which many aircraft captains established between themselves and their crews. Many a wireless operator was abruptly silenced if he ventured to offer information or advice in the face of obvious difficulties. A succession of radio bearings, obtained with difficulty by the radio operator and passed in a note to the captain, might be discarded unread. In the twenties and thirties the idea that the captain of an aircraft was part of a team, who although

having ultimate authority adopted a relaxed and communicative attitude towards his crew, was not always the case. Such domineering attitudes lasted on the flight deck well into the 1950s.

Any review of the many different cockpits designed, produced or even abandoned since 1903 leaves one with an overall impression of a lack of standardization. During the first 40 years of cockpit development there appears to have been much confusion among a wealth of ideas.

Every aircraft design team has had to wrestle with a number of conflicting options. These include: continuing to use cockpit shapes, details and equipment from an existing aircraft — or starting with a 'clean sheet' and a list of new equipment. Usually a compromise has been necessary and the new has been combined with the old.

Historically, design offices have shown a less than uniform attitude towards considering the physical needs and limitations of the pilot; and even when a design

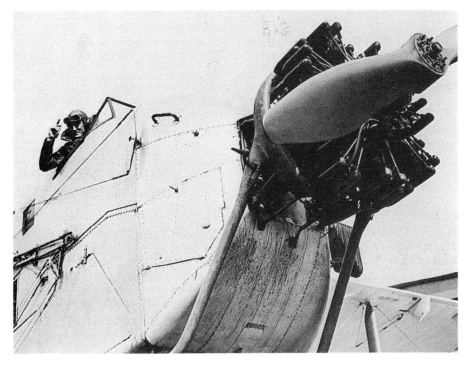

'Start number three'. But in those days — 1925 — engines were not necessarily numbered from left to right, as became the custom from about 1940 onwards. (John Stroud)

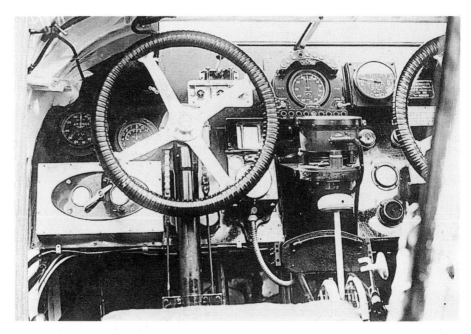

A.W. Argosy circa 1928. Airspeed and height indicators partly obscured by other equipment; direct drive TEL recording tachometer for the middle engine; transparent panels above the instrument panel. A Reid Control Indicator is mounted top centre, which incorporated an air-driven gyro to detect the rate of turn and a mercury-in-tube with electrical contacts for bank. This provided indications of airspeed, lateral level (the arc of lights at the top) and the rate of turn in degrees per unit of time (the row of lights at the bottom of the instrument case). (John Stroud)

team did add to its list 'The pilot: his needs and problems', intuition and guesswork often dominated the design process. Admittedly each design office did have the advice of an experienced test pilot.

The test pilots employed by each of the aircraft constructors undoubtedly held their appointments because of their experience and skill. But their qualities were usually above those of the average pilot, with the result that they easily overcame any shortcomings in the design of the cockpit and its equipment. Many of what we now describe as bad design details in cockpits of the past were initially just a minor annoyance to the test pilot and not worth commenting upon. Subsequently the line pilots also overcame the problems of reaching for a knuckle-grazing vital control in the dark with one engine failing on take-off with a full load. But the chances of an error still remained. Since then, times have changed; today the line pilots 'get in the act' at the drawing board stage of a new aircraft and there is a wealth of written good design practice from which to develop a good 'front office'.

Individual pilots pride themselves on overcoming difficult situations, and walking away from a successful landing after an arduous flight often forget about the cockpit deficiencies which had contributed to their difficulties. Later, when in discussion with other pilots, they may 'moan and groan' about their aircraft. If all agree, collectively pilots will urge action. On the other hand, self-esteem may predominate, any discontent being dismissed as 'That's the sort of thing we're paid to overcome'.

Night, cloud and fog

In the beginning, when there were no, or few instruments, aviation did not borrow immediately from other forms of transport; for even at sea, on the road and on the railway there were not many to go by.

Instrument development has tended to follow the development of other parts of aviation. Each progression in aircraft performance and utility has usually required some form of instrumentation. In the same way that increasing height had required the development of the altimeter, increasing speeds required the development of better and better airspeed indicators. As the aircraft became more effective as a vehicle and it was necessary to provide the pilot with the means of taking full advantage of its capabilities, then more and better instruments had to be provided.

Instrument development prior to 1914 was slow compared with the progress made with airframes and engines. After a tentative start, military aviation was well established by the middle of 1915. Instruments were improved in number and quality to meet he increasing performance and versatility of aircraft employed by the warring nations.

During this period in aircraft development a number of inventors were busy with mechanisms incorporating a gyroscope. The gyroscope already formed the principal component in naval fire control systems. However the use of gyroscopic mechanisms in aircraft instruments was frustrated by a shortage of suitable materials and precision production resources. This applied to many other types of instrument. For example Kollsman in the USA, one of the more important names in instrument develop-

ment, had to get mechanisms for his first series of altimeters made in Switzerland.

As already mentioned, the earliest altimeters for use in aircraft were the scientist's aneroid recording barometer with a circular chart cylinder on which a pen marked variations in barometric pressure against time. Pilots could also carry a balloonist's 'pocket watch' altimeter.

In the 1920s RAF aircraft in which a pupil was under instruction had long white cloth 'streamers' attached to the outermost interplane struts. These indicated that other pilots should keep clear. This is mentioned here because the streamers provided an indication of the reverse flow which occurs over a wing which is stalled, and thus they might be classed as an instrument.

Few pilots are capable of stable blind flying without reference to instruments. The human senses can be deceived by apparent sensations of aircraft movement. The most obvious is the sensation of turning in one direction immediately after completing a turn in the other direction.

In the 1920s instrument flying was in the early stages of development. Air forces took the subject very seriously

Below left *'Anti-clockwise' altimeter circa 1920. In addition to the height scale the dial carries indications in degrees Celsius of the boiling point of water for use when checking the operation of a liquid-cooled engine.* (Smiths Industries)

Below right *Airspeed indicator, typical of the type installed in British aircraft in the latter half of the First World War.* (Smiths Industries)

Cockpit of the DH Moth: very simple engine controls, with six instruments including the aperiodic compass. (British Aerospace)

because it was realized that an air war could not be postponed or cancelled because the pilots were unable to stay on course or the right way up in cloud or in reduced visibility. The RAF, for example, instituted a programme of investigating the problems of instrument flight — with the Central Flying School, as usual, setting the pace.

The air force problem of operating in low visibility is underlined if we consider a formation of aircraft trying to keep station. In daylight and in cloud it is necessary to keep the distance between the wingtips of adjacent aircraft to less than 20 feet.

Any history of the pilot's place and his instruments must include the name of W.E.P. Johnson. He was among the few pilots in the 1920s who made a thorough study of the ways in which a pilot reacted to sensations of aircraft movement when attempting to fly 'blind'. His research disclosed that even among experienced pilots none could fly in cloud or under the 'hood' without getting into a spin within a

few minutes: eight as a maximum.

Although these pilots recovered the aircraft from a spin, it immediately entered another. The problem was essentially one of the perceived acceleration forces. As the pilot moved the controls to stop the spin, the accelerating forces applied to the semi-circular canals within his ears produced a sensation of entering a spin in the opposite direction to the first — even though the aircraft had stopped spinning.

Flight Lieutenant (as he then was) Johnson's research emphasized the value of the recently developed gyro-based turn indicators. The RAF Central Flying School curriculum therefore taught pilots to concentrate on the instruments and to ignore 'seat of the pants' sensations when flying 'blind'.

In the USA William Ocker of the Air Corps had made similar studies to those of Johnson into the effects leading to pilot disorientation. In 1928 he developed a simulator for teaching pilots to rely on their instruments rather than on their perceived sensations of aircraft movement. The technique of concentrating on needle, ball and airspeed was taught, i.e. in the absence of an artificial horizon and vertical speed indicator, concentrating on the needle and the ball of the turn and slip indicator and indicated airspeed. From this technique and the development of other equipment was established sound instrument flying procedures. Civil aviation in the USA took advantage of this before the military. Not until 1943 was the skill of instrument flying part of the training of all American service pilots.

Another of the ideas that arose from a worldwide interest in the development of 'blind flying' equipment and techniques was the extendable hood for the pupil's cockpit, introduced in 1925 by the Farman School of Flying, Paris.

One of the earliest attempts at a blind flying panel was to be found in the Hawker Tomtit of 1928. This was a year before the first take-off, circuit and landing under 'the hood' in the USA. The Tomtit trainer for the RAF had a Reid & Sigrist instrument panel which included the recently introduced turn and bank, or turn and slip, indicator by which a pilot could perfect co-ordinated turns. A perfectly co-ordinated turn is one in which the aircraft is banked at an angle at which it slips neither inward nor outward during the turn. In an open cockpit during a correctly co-ordinated turn the pilot senses equal airflow on both sides of his face. With instrument flying becoming a standard part of a pilot's training and qualifications in the RAF, the Hawker Tomtit was equipped with a hood which could be pulled over the student's cockpit.

Although the Tomtit was designed as a replacement for the Avro 504N (Lynx Avro), the older aircraft remained in service for a few more years. In 1931 the 504s were also equipped with Reid & Sigrist turn and bank indicators as well as a hood for the pupil's cockpit. As late as 1933 the Central Flying School's 'travelling circus', which gave instrument flying demonstrations, was still using the 504s.

The turn and bank indicator did not come into flying school or squadron use overnight. The whole process took from about 1928 to 1934. For example, Bristol Bulldog fighters were not equipped with turn and bank indicators as standard. Some Hawker Furies which entered service in 1931 were so equipped.

Although the turn and bank indicator enabled a pilot to execute precise turns, he still had to rely on his other instruments, such as airspeed and engine rpm, to hold level flight or a desired rate

Avro 504K Lynx, for many years the principal RAF trainer; the 'blind' flying hood can be seen folded down behind the pupil's cockpit. (via Aeroplane Monthly)

Hawker Tomtit trainer, circa 1931, with a Reid and Sigrist turn and slip indicator and the fore and aft inclinometer which, together with the other instruments, enabled flight to continue when the horizon was obscured. (Smiths Industries)

of climb or descent. In 1932 the precursor of today's RAF Institute of Aviation Medicine installed a 'cockpit' of controls and instruments in the fuselage of a Vickers Victoria of the Central Flying School. This cockpit had no windows and, to make things harder for its 'guinea pig' occupant, it faced aft. Hence the pupil pilot received sensations of aircraft movement completely opposite to those he normally experienced, so he had to pay even greater attention to what the blind flying instruments told him to do.

Lindbergh

On 22 May 1927 Lindbergh landed his Ryan monoplane on the airfield at Le Bourget, Paris, after a 28-hour transatlantic solo flight. Lindbergh had equipped the *Spirit of St Louis* with the most advanced instruments available at the time but the control interface was, by present day standards, crude. Perhaps the lack of comfort and automatic systems helped to keep him awake.

The cockpit of the *Spirit of St Louis* was equipped with eleven instruments, which in 1927 was four more than would

have been fitted to the majority of contemporary single-engine monoplanes. There was only one gyroscopic instrument — a turn and slip indicator. Dominating the instrument panel was the Pioneer earth inductor compass, which was the primary navigation aid. The altimeter, rpm and airspeed indicators formed, with the compass, an approximately rectangular grouping: the sixth position, top left, was not an instrument as such but the viewing aperture of the periscope by which Lindbergh could see ahead along the left side of the fuselage and engine. His otherwise normal forward view through a windscreen was obstructed by two fuel tanks, one of 208 gallons and the other of 86 gallons capacity.

The lower centre part of the instrument panel carried a lateral and fore-and-aft, bubble-in-glass-tube inclinometers. Under the lower edge of the panel was the distribution manifold for the fuel system, which included a test cock with open funnel leading to a drain pipe.

In 1927, there being little, if any, study made of cockpit design and human factors, it followed that the arrangement of the instruments was to no particular scheme. It is interesting to reflect that one of Lindbergh's greatest hazards was sleep; as suggested, we might conjecture that had the cockpit and its equipment been designed with human factors in mind then this would have produced a low workload, comfortable cockpit, which might have induced sleep far more rapidly than one in which the pilot had to concentrate on maintaining control. Even in what, to our eyes, is a crude cockpit, Lindbergh had to devise methods of waking himself should he 'nod off'.

Will the flight deck of the future be such a comfortable, relaxing environment that means will have to be devised to keep the pilots alert?

The difficulties of Lindbergh's transatlantic flight are described in detail in his book *The Spirit of St Louis*. In the thirteenth hour of the flight Lindbergh has to decide between continuing to fly by reference to the stars or to rely on instruments alone: 'Why try to hold on to those stars? Why not start in now on in-struments. After all they were put there so that I could fly through fog. This game of hide and seek with a half-dozen stars is child's play. But if I start flying blind, God only knows how many hours of it lie ahead. It might go on through the entire night — the monotony of flying with my eyes always on the instrument board, the strain of flying by intellect alone, forcing the unruly senses of the body to follow the doubted orders of the mind — the endless bringing of one needle after another back to its proper position, and then finding that all except the one my eyes hold tight have strayed off again. *The Spirit of St Louis* is too unstable to fly well on instruments. It's fast, and it has greater range than any plane that flies; but it's high-strung, and balanced on a pin point. If I relax pressure on stick or rudder for an instant, the nose will veer off course.'

Doolittle

On 24 September 1929, only 26 years after the Wrights' historic flight, Lieu-

Instrument panel of Lindbergh's 'Spirit of St Louis'. Because of the maximum size fuel tank between engine and cockpit, Lindbergh's only forward view was through the periscope which protruded to the left. (Author)

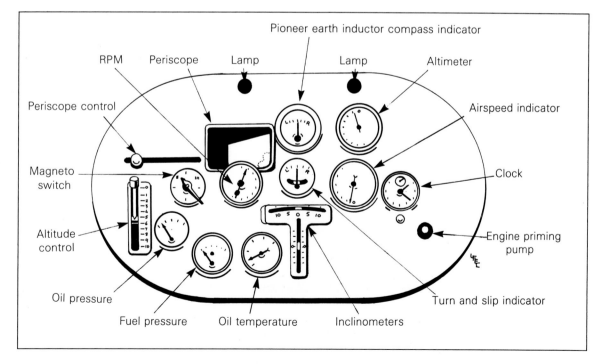

Lieutenant, later General, James Doolittle in the cockpit of the Consolidated NY-2 in which he successfully demonstrated a complete take-off, circuit and landing 'under the hood'. (Kollsman)

tenant James Doolittle was airborne in a Consolidated NY–2 single-engine biplane. Doolittle flew the aircraft from take-off, round the circuit and back to a landing without being able to see the horizon or the ground. The hooded cockpit was equipped with the most advanced instruments available at the time.

A safety pilot, Lieutenant Ben Kelsey, sat in the forward open cockpit but did not have to touch the controls throughout the 15-minute flight.

This was to become, like Lindbergh's, another historic flight; particularly in the progress towards flying in all weather and visibility conditions.

Doolittle was not only one of the foremost competition pilots of the 1920s and the following decade, but he was intensely interested in the whole subject of instrument flying and the loss of spatial orientation experienced by pilots attempting to fly 'blind'. He was convinced that the recently developed gyroscopic instruments were the key to the problem. With the backing of the wealthy Guggenheimer family and working with Paul Kollsman, the developer of the sensitive altimeter, and with Elmer Sperry, the gyroscopic systems pioneer, Doolittle evolved techniques for 'blind' flying. After more than a hundred proving flights he was ready on that September day to demonstrate a complete flight 'under the hood'.

Kollsman sensitive altimeter developed for Doolittle's 'blind' flight of 24 September 1929. (Kollsman)

Left *The instruments in Doolittle's NY-2. The special radio beacon direction finder is the octagonally shaped instrument in the lower left corner of the photograph. The Sperry artificial horizon is extreme left in the bottom row of instruments. There are three compass indicators.* (Kollsman)

Below *Doolittle's 1929 flight: typical related indications of three of the instruments in the NY-2's hooded cockpit.* (Author)

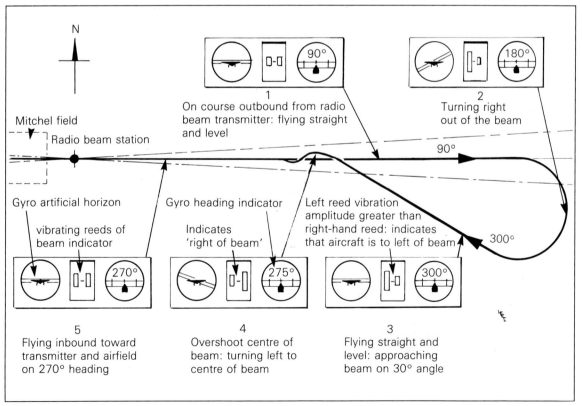

N

Mitchel field
Radio beam station

1
On course outbound from radio beam transmitter: flying straight and level

2
Turning right out of the beam

90°

300°

Gyro artificial horizon

vibrating reeds of beam indicator

Gyro heading indicator

Indicates 'right of beam'

Left reed vibration amplitude greater than right-hand reed: indicates that aircraft is to left of beam

5
Flying inbound toward transmitter and airfield on 270° heading

4
Overshoot centre of beam: turning left to centre of beam

3
Flying straight and level: approaching beam on 30° angle

The NY–2 taxied out, took off, completed a circuit and landed. Doolittle followed the indications of the radio guidance system and used the recently developed flight instruments to maintain the correct attitude and to descend at a steady and precise rate toward a landing back on Mitchell Field. For its time the specially equipped NY–2 had more than the usual number of instruments. They included: rpm, oil temperature and pressure, Sperry gyro artificial horizon and direction indicator, generator current and voltage, compass, turn and slip indicator, airspeed, standard altimeter, vertical speed plus a special Kollsman 0–20,000-feet altimeter.

That innovative flight may not have been perfect, as Doolittle admitted, but it laid the foundation for a number of techniques which are still in use in 1990.

One of the key instruments on Doolittle's instrument panel in 1929 was the Sperry artificial horizon. This was a

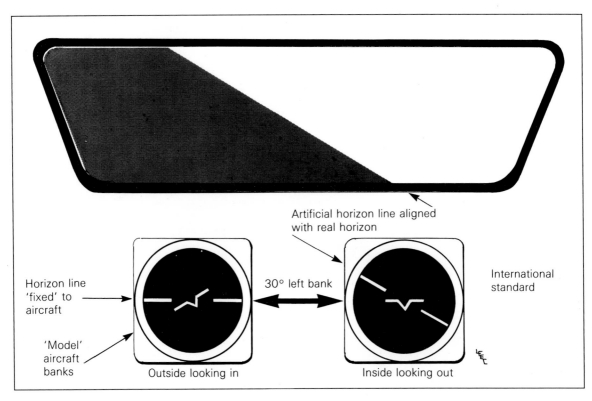

Artificial horizon line aligned with real horizon

Horizon line 'fixed' to aircraft

'Model' aircraft banks

Outside looking in

30° left bank

Inside looking out

International standard

distinct advance in the evolution of flight instruments. Before the development of the artificial horizon pilots had to rely for attitude information on bubble inclinometers, of which there may have been as many as three in the cockpit. Obviously these could not be used with much degree of precision and therefore flight in cloud, or at any time when the horizon was obscured, became either difficult or even dangerous.

This early Sperry artificial horizon had a small fixed symbol of an aircraft. Interestingly the aircraft depicted was a single-engine, high-wing monoplane similar to the Ryan flown by Lindbergh. The instrument also had a presentation which later became known as the 'inside looking out' arrangement because the aircraft symbol was fixed relative to the instrument case and the instrument panel. The artificial line of the horizon moved. The alternative display — a fixed horizon line against which moves the aircraft symbol — was considered at the time and at intervals during the past 60 years. This is classified as the 'outside looking in' arrangement. A version is used in many modern American aircraft as a 'turn co-ordinator'. The outside looking in concept was revived in the 1980s for advanced fighter head-up displays so that the pilot could 'see' a model of his aircraft flying against the artificial view of the world. An analogy is the computer game in which the operator has to fly an aircraft so as to avoid hostile aircraft and missiles.

Jason

On 5 May 1930 Amy Johnson set off on her solo flight from England to Australia. This was the era of pioneering long-distance flights. As with other aircraft, her's was frail in the face of storms and turbulence. The navigational aids were either rudimentary or non-existent over the greater part of the route. Her DH Moth *Jason* had an open cockpit and very few instruments. Navigation was

primarily by dead (deduced) reckoning with much reliance on maintaining visual contact with the ground when over land. After Calcutta much of the route passed over the sea.

The all-up weight limit of the Moth did not allow for additional instruments, particularly as Amy Johnson loaded *Jason* with a spare propeller and a comprehensive kit of tools in addition to medicines, mosquito net, sun helmet and revolver. Her maps and charts, arranged as strips, were mounted on rollers for ease of use. Her primary heading aid was the British type aperiodic compass. She had no radio, either for communication or navigation. *Jason*'s cockpit and its instruments were little different from other flying club machines.

She was dependent, as were all pilots, on checking position by reference to ground features. This is emphasized by her own description of the final phase of the approach to Rangoon: '... I then attempted to cross the mountains near Akyab ... Climbing above one layer of clouds, I threaded my way among their enormous piled up masses, expecting every minute to run into a mountain I could not see. After half an hour I calculated I ought to be on the farther side, so began to come down through the clouds. It seemed almost a miracle that at this moment the clouds should part, and I saw far below the gleam of a large river. Circling round and round whilst gliding down, in order to keep this precious bit of river in sight, I was at last just over it and following its course southwards. I knew of course that it must be the Irrawaddy and I was able to pick up my exact position on the map.'

More and better instruments

The 1930s were years of rapid technical development in both military and civil aviation. The monoplane, all-metal construction, and equipment to enable schedule flights to continue irrespective of

Sperry artificial horizon used by Doolittle in 1929. This was the progenitor of tens of thousands of similar instruments used as the key element of 'blind' flying panels. (Sperry)

'Inside looking out' — the artificial horizon. (Author)

Above *Dornier Do X of 1929 with fully enclosed flight deck.* (Dornier)

Right *Lockheed Model 10 Electra. Flight instruments are grouped on the centre of the crackle-paint-finish panel; engine instruments are concentrated in front of the first pilot. The fuel tank selector and the engine fuel cock selector are similar in shape and close together on the back of the central pedestal.* (Lockheed)

weather and visibility conditions — these were ushering out the open cockpit strut and wire biplanes which had descended from the Handley Page 0/400 and the Vickers Vimy. Cockpits were starting to fill up with instruments, and engine instruments in particular were being installed in front of the pilot rather than out on the engine nacelles. Yet in 1930 the instrument manufacturers were still producing outside air temperature indicators which could be strapped to the interplane struts of a biplane. This is another example of the slow progress made with the development of remote indicating systems during the 1920s.

The steady increase in the number of instruments in the cockpit, to keep pace with the steady improvements in aircraft versatility and performance, was an ad hoc process. Little attention was given to the fundamental purpose of the instruments. Namely, that individually and collectively they had to give the pilot unambiguous information without distracting him from other tasks. Other tasks included keeping a visual lookout. Unfortunately too many instruments, and the ways in which they were arranged on the panels, left much to chance.

By the early 1930s the demand for more accurate and reliable flight instruments increased as air transport

endeavoured to expand. Flight instruments are those needed to maintain the desired heading, attitude, vertical speed, height and, when turning, the correct angle of bank and rate of turn.

However, the development of instruments still lagged behind the ambitions of the aircraft operators. Even as late as 1937 new aircraft were being equipped with altimeters whose accuracy was greatly affected because they 'read' the air pressure of an enclosed cockpit. This pressure might be less than that of the air through which the aircraft was flying. Therefore the altimeter might indicate, incorrectly, that the aircraft was higher than it actually was. One of the prototype Hurricanes and its valuable test pilot were nearly destroyed because of this, until then, unrealized effect. This incident occurred during a descent through cloud to regain 'contact'. Thereafter the altimeter connections were rearranged.

In the early 1930s electrical fuel contents gauges were developed as production items. These were a considerable advance, in both accuracy and simplicity of installation, over the existing methods of checking fuel contents — some of which included pipes carrying fuel passing through the cockpit.

Significantly in the history of air transport, the new electrical fuel contents indicating system was selected for the Handley Page four-engine airliner, the HP42, which became one of the best known large biplanes in the service of Imperial Airways from 1932 onwards.

By 1935 direct reading fuel contents indicating systems were no longer considered desirable, and electrical remote reading tank contents systems were fitted to a number of different aircraft types including the Gloster Gladiator, the DH86 and the Singapore III. It was at about this time that the pressure on pilots, operators and others to fly in all visibility conditions encouraged the fitting of artificial horizons. Catalogues of the mid-1930s featured this essential aid to instrument flying.

CHAPTER FOUR

OPEN OR CLOSED

The enclosed 'front office'

As we have seen, the open cockpit remained a feature of civil transport aircraft until about 1930. Yet semi- and fully-enclosed positions had been considered and sometimes applied, from the earliest years of aviation. Sikorsky's, for its time giant, Ilia Mouremetz four-engine bomber had an enclosed pilot's place. The Felixstowe F series of flying boats included examples with semi-enclosed cockpits. Although these aircraft were military types, in the absence of civil aviation in those years they can serve as examples of what a civil aircraft might have looked like.

Prior to 1930 Boeing introduced the 80A, 18-passenger, biplane with an enclosed 'front office'. Following representations from the pilots the next version had an open cockpit. This, of course, is not an example of 'bloody mindedness' on the part of the pilots but a reflection on the difficulties of air navigation at that time. It is remarkable too in the light of pilots in the twenties and thirties not having a strong position from which to argue about technical and operating matters in civil aviation.

On the subject of the role of the pilot in civil aircraft cockpit design, it is important to recall that in Britain only the manufacturers and the Martlesham Heath test pilots had any say in what went where in the cockpit. Civil airworthiness requirements both in Britain and other countries did not necessarily go into great detail on the subject. The Air Ministry publication *AP 970*, which included some cockpit requirements, over the years gradually acquired more references to the cockpit as aviation expanded.

Both civil and military aircraft design and competition, particularly in Britain, were limited by financial resources to making the most of what a company had. There was little money available for research into new cockpit equipment and layout.

The single- and two-seat aircraft cockpits of the 1920s were usually open to the slipstream environment. Sporting and display pilots still braved the stinging blast with only a small glass screen to mitigate some of the uncomfortable effects. That they would not have it otherwise is to miss the point: enclosed cockpits were not even to be found on the big multi-engined aircraft.

For a number of reasons the fully enclosed cockpit was slow to emerge as a common feature of civil transport aircraft. As already described, most pilots depended on the 'wind on the cheek' as an 'instrument'. In the absence of reliable wipers and heated glass they did not

Loiré et Olivier 21, a two-pilot open cockpit passenger aircraft operated by Air France in the 1920s. (John Stroud)

necessarily want to be totally enclosed. After all, the average motorist of those years dressed like a pilot and preferred an open cockpit.

However, towards the end of the first decade of peacetime flying a number of civil aircraft, particularly transports, were entering service with enclosed 'front offices'.

In the 1920s German cockpits were close to the 'sharp end' — if you can call the lumpy engines of those times 'sharp'. The pioneer all-metal Junkers F13s of DLH were not only monoplanes at a time when the biplane still ruled the skies, but the cockpit was fully enclosed. The shape of the forward windows obviously exercised considerable skill on the part of the metal workers. The F13s windscreen reduced drag by its rakish angle; in contrast the Fokker F2s of Deutsche Aero Lloyd copied automobile practice and had a vertical windscreen.

In 1927 DLH (Lufthansa) introduced two new Albatros L73s on the night-sleeper service between Berlin and Konigsberg which connected with a flight to Moscow. The L73 carried eight passengers in semi-reclining chairs. The two pilots sat in the comfort — for its time — of a fully enclosed cockpit with forward windows of a shape which anticipated aircraft design of 20 years later. With a cruising speed of only 78 knots there was time in which to pick out each of the rotating searchlight beacons which were spaced every 15 miles along the route.

A contemporary of the Albatross L73 was the French L&O 21 18-passenger, twin-engine, biplane. Although similar in design and size the L&O seated the pilot in an open cockpit above and between the two passenger cabins. In normal flight attitude the pilot had a good all-round view; but not such a good view ahead when the tailskid was on the ground. The later version, the L&O 213, was advertised, using Franglais, as 'une avion dancing'. The dancing referred, not to the flying characteristics of the aircraft, but to the facility afforded the passengers for passing the time between Paris and London. The pilot, lonely in his on-top cockpit, must have had mixed feelings about the effect le Foxtrot and le Jazz

DH Gipsy Coupé Moth of 1929. Not all pilots would put up with an open cockpit, particularly if they could afford an expensive modification such as this. (via Aeroplane Monthly)

Below *A rare DH three-seats-in-tandem modification.* (British Aerospace)

were having on the fore and aft trim.

The Breguet 280T eight-seater had a side-by-side, two-pilot, enclosed cockpit immediately behind the single 450-hp engine. There was no door to the forward bulkhead of the passenger cabin: this afforded the occupants a clear view of the pilots at work; and on occasions two pairs of white knuckles wrestling with the controls.

Placing the pilots in direct communication with the passengers was considered to be acceptable.

In the late 1920s the rules of the road, keep right, and the left-hand circuit, were well established. Associated with the left-hand circuit was the British practice of specifying take-offs from the left side of a field and landings on the right side. These rules engendered specific lookout practices on the part of pilots. In the absence of positive airfield control, except at the larger and busier aerodromes such as Le Bourget and Croydon, it was essential to keep a sharp lookout at all times when taxying, taking off and landing: otherwise there could be some expensive splintering of wood and tearing of fabric, not to mention the cost of a new propeller. Once again we have an example of

why pilots in general were averse to fully enclosed cockpits.

Although radio communication was developed to a reasonable standard by the end of the First World War, not all aircraft were equipped with receivers or transmitters in the 1920s. To be certain of communicating with aircraft flying in the vicinity of an airfield, over the years a set of ground symbols was developed. These were used in conjunction with flags and shapes hoisted on halyards.

On approaching an airfield the pilot had to read the information displayed in the 'signals square'. Various symbols indicated the handedness of the circuit, left- or right-hand; others the direction of take-off and landing in use — before the era of runways not necessarily in the same direction, red and yellow markers indicated that landings were prohibited and others that certain parts of the airfield were unsuitable for landings.

Control symbols and flags were used for the early competitive aviation meetings. During the First World War armies and air forces developed systems of ground-to-air communication usually using white panels which could be arranged to convey different messages. Even in the

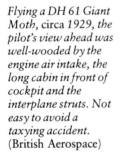

Flying a DH 61 Giant Moth, circa 1929, the pilot's view ahead was well-wooded by the engine air intake, the long cabin in front of cockpit and the interplane struts. Not easy to avoid a taxying accident. (British Aerospace)

1930s uncertain or non-existent radio links with ground forces meant that the RAF had to rely on a Popham Panel. This was a large dark blue cloth which was laid out on the ground. Attached to this background sheet were a number of panels which when turned over formed a number of different white symbols.

Once away from an airfield the civil pilot was usually also away from any form of air traffic control. It was not until 1935 in Britain that a zonal type of separation was instituted: essentially, this required aircraft to be flown at heights related to the quadrants of the compass.

A number of British and French passenger aircraft types had the pilot's position above and behind the passenger cabin. This was an obvious arrangement because it kept the disposable load — the passengers — seated close to the aircraft's centre of gravity. Notable examples from the formative years of civil aviation are: the DH18, operated by A.T. & Travel, with the pilot's forward view obstructed by the fuselage-mounted upper plane centre section, and the Breguet 14T of CMA and the Potez 9 of CFRNA, which had a similar arrangement of pilot at the back; perhaps for historical purposes we might call this the 'Hansom Cab' cockpit. With the forward view well 'wooded', to use a nautical term, no pilot was going to suffer an enclosed cockpit.

It was not only passengers that were carried betwixt engine and pilot. The mails usually travelled that way, particularly in the United States. In the years of the graceful biplanes, the Douglas M–4s of Western Air Express and the Pitcairn Mailwing of Colonial Eastern Airways, the mail was carried in a compartment in front of the pilot's open cockpit.

An even larger 'Hansom Cab' design was the Boeing 40A, which carried both passengers and mail. As already mentioned, the air mail services in the USA made an important contribution to aviation technology. The goal of regular mail flights encouraged the development of more reliable engines, better instruments and more navigational aids.

To avoid getting too far ahead in the history it is important to note that the emerging German air transport system did not make use of the 'Hansom Cab' layout for single-engine civil aircraft.

Cockpits at this time, particularly those in which the pilot's feet were up against the engine, would not have won a Design Council award: they were utilitarian in the extreme and in the history of transport as a whole might be classed with the crude footplate of the early steam locomotive. Naturally there were some advantages: for example, the pilot was not likely to confuse the main fuel cock with some other lever, for its accompanying plumbing was there for all to see and smell.

Not all designs used the basic principle of keeping the disposable load close to the centre of gravity. In the Latecoere 17 the pilot's cockpit was between engine and cabin, a position which ensured that the pilot's head was immediately under the centre section. It kept the rain off whilst he was waiting to start the engine but allowed only limited arcs of view above eyebrow level.

The twenties were an era of contrast in aircraft designs, with a great number of different types: some single, some twin, some tri- and others quadri-engined; some monoplanes, others biplanes including sesquiplanes: open cockpits and closed cockpits: cockpits in front, cockpits on top and cockpits towards the tail. But a few were precursors to the future. In the USA the 1927 Lockheed Vega and its successor the Orion set new standards in design and performance, and the Orion possessed a completely enclosed cockpit.

Three engines

1930 is the year in which a number of new designs emerged for use on the expanding airways of the world. Although structural techniques had advanced

significantly, engines were still limited in power to around 500 hp. This set a problem for the aerodynamicists and weight control specialists, but it also set a problem for the cockpit designer, for the limited engine power usually meant adopting a three-engine arrangement. An engine in the nose restricted the forward view for the pilots as well as sometimes liberally covering the windscreen with oil.

Most famous perhaps of the aircraft of the tri-motor era of the early thirties was the Ju52. The /3m version of this Junkers corrugated-skinned series of aircraft had a cockpit with three of most things. Much has been written about the design and construction of the aircraft, but not necessarily about the 'front office'. The first point to make is that even on a dark night it could not be mistaken for other than a German aircraft of the time. There was a general look of robustness about the controls and the instrument panels. Other details emphasized that the Ju52 was part of a national airline (Lufthansa)

which, albeit with war in mind, had developed aids to navigation and landing which, with variations, would remain in use for over 20 years: for example the Lorenz approach and landing aid system. In parallel with the USA, German industry had developed remote reading and radio compasses. These were a feature in German cockpits long before British operators had completely abandoned the large P series magnetic compasses. These often caused a problem in cockpit design when trying to locate them so that they could be seen and reached by the pilot.

Many pilots who flew the Ju52 commented on the contrast between the basic simplicity of the design — fixed undercarriage and fixed pitch propellers — and the elaborate cockpit with, for its time, a mass of levers, knobs, small knurled 'ship's engine room' wheels, and a profusion of switches and instruments. All these were disposed in a somewhat haphazard arrangement. (Again, it must be borne in mind that the Ju52, like other types, had a long life in airline and air

Far left *The instrument panel of a Lockheed Orion single-engine monoplane transport of 1931, whose speed and retractable undercarriage placed it well ahead of others. The Sperry panel dominates the instrument layout, with the flight instruments above. The hydraulic actuators of the automatic pilot are set below the instrument panel. The manifold (boost) pressure gauge is installed with the nominal reading at nine o'clock; similarly the airspeed indicator is installed so that two critical speeds are at three and nine o'clock respectively to simplify the pilot's instrument scan. A typical American magneto selector switch can be seen at the bottom left of the instrument panel. The wing flap position indicator is notable for its extremely small size. The wire frame depending from the top of the windscreen is an aid to straight and level flight in good visibility. (Lockheed)*

Left *Of advanced design for 1925, including its fully enclosed flight deck — the Fokker FVII 3m tri-motor transport. (Swiss Air)*

*Ju52 3m of
Lufthansa: a well-
fenestrated pilot's
place.* (Lufthansa)

force service and that there were many variants, each of which exhibited variations in the number, type and position of controls and instruments.)

The cockpit of the Ju52 was well above the line of the top of the nacelle of the middle engine, so that the pilots had a good view forward, to both sides and above. The cockpit canopy was formed from 17 separate glazed panels.

The Fokker tri-motor types, which had inaugurated so many important air routes at the end of the previous decade, continued in use in new and improved versions during the thirties. One of these was the F.VII/3m, which in 1931 had comparatively extensive instrumentation. At the same time, this Fokker type exhibited two features typical of civil aviation practice of those years: the blind flying instruments on the centre of the main panel, and engine instruments on the inboard sides of the nacelles. In the FVII/3m the flight deck instruments included those for the centre engine, which meant that the pilots always had in front of them an indication of how that engine

was behaving, but had to depend on being able to read the nacelle-mounted instruments for the other engines by looking out of the side windows of the cockpit. Co-ordination of engine settings was undoubtedly difficult with a fragmented display of information.

Another Fokker type for which there is a detailed record of the flight deck equipment was the F32, a four-engined airliner (two pulling, two pushing) developed in the USA by Fokker's North American company. The throttles on the central pedestal in this case were arranged with the outers controlling the front engines and the inners the 'pushers'. The pilot in the left-hand seat was given compass, airspeed, height and vertical speed indicators plus a transverse inclinometer and a turn and bank indicator, whereas his co-pilot, typically, was not given any flight instruments to look at.

The Fokker FXX of 1933 had a fully enclosed flight deck with seats for first and second pilots and a radio operator. It had dual controls, flight instruments in front of the first pilot and had an early ex-

Left *The typical German attention to the detail finish of instruments and their panels and to controls is immediately apparent on the Ju 52 3m flight deck. The second pilot, on the right, also doubled as radio operator, hence the winch for the trailing aerial.* (John Stroud)

Below *Ford tri-motor, circa 1928. Although this is a modern re-built aircraft, the typical reverse-raked, vee-shaped windscreen has been retained.* (American Airlines)

Above *An unusual tandem pilots' seating arrangement — the Fokker XXII, circa 1934. (via Aeroplane Monthly)*

ample of a separate flight engineer's station. However, despite these advanced design features, there was two odd features: one, the flaps could be selected only by the first pilot because the control was to the left of his seat; two, the retractable undercarriage, which was hauled up and let down manually, was operated by the flight engineer by means of a large wheel and therefore inaccessible to the pilots. Fragmentation of responsibility for such basic control functions was to become unthinkable in the further evolution of the pilot's place after the Second World War.

At the end of the 1920s and on into the 30s, the incentive of national pride produced a number of high-performance air-

craft as competitors in the Schneider Trophy speed circuit and the National Air Races in the USA.

The cockpits of competitive aircraft were not usually representative of the state of the technology because of the special conditions which applied. The aircraft entered for the Schneider Trophy, for example, had minimum-size cockpits and afforded the pilot neither comfort nor a good view ahead.

Among the competitors for the 1931 Schneider Trophy was the RAF High Speed Flight, which retained the Trophy for Britain. The RAF's Supermarine S6B had a cockpit which denied the pilot virtually any view ahead. To reduce drag the cross section of the fuselage was no greater than that of the engine: the drag of even a small windscreen could not be allowed for.

The 13 Trophy meetings between 1913 and 1931 were run anti-clockwise so that all turns round the markers and pylons were to the left. The powerful engines of the 1929 and 1931 entrants produced a strong torque reaction which tended to roll the aircraft to the left. During take-off it was often difficult to keep the aircraft straight. In addition to not being able to see directly ahead, the view to one side was obscured by spray. The application of too much power would make the port-side float dig in during the long take-off run, even though more fuel was carried in the starboard float than in the port, and some aircraft had more lifting surface for the port wing. The Supermarine S6B and the other Trophy aircraft did not contribute any significant changes to cockpit design and equipment; in contrast to their outstanding contribution to engine performance and to airframe design.

The 1930s were a time for a new look at the 'front office'. From that year on few new designs of civil transport aircraft had open cockpits — though the open 'pilot's place' continued in use in small private and sporting aircraft. The enclosed 'front office' also became a standard feature of

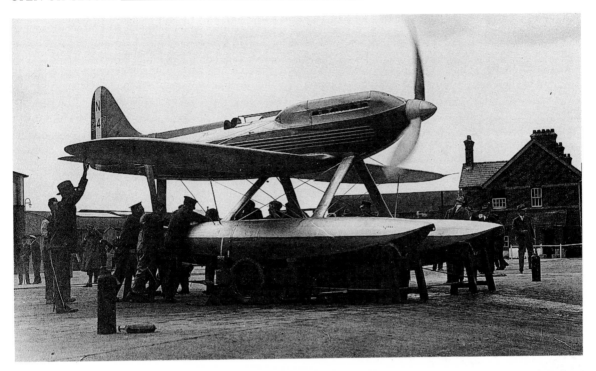

Left Ju G38, circa 1930. *The flight deck is integrated with the passenger cabin, which is also extended outboard into the thick-section wing. Powerful landing lights are set in the tip of the nose.* (John Stroud)

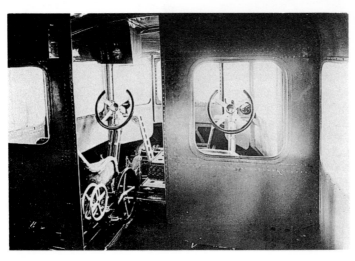

most of the larger aircraft at this time because increasing recognition was being given to the importance of getting rid of drag-producing excrescences and openings, of which the open cockpit was one of the greatest contributors. The comfort of the pilot was not necessarily uppermost in the thoughts of the designer and operator.

Ahoy there

Until the 1940s, the flying boat, both civil and air force types, was a familiar part of the aviation scene. Although the flying boat pilot's cockpit needs to be considered its equipment was little different from that of land-based machines of a similar size. The principal differences stemmed from the need to give the crew access to mooring and anchoring gear. This usually required the provision of a mooring hatch forward of the flight deck. The other notable difference was the use of pendant — 'overhead' — throttles in many high-wing flying boats; of which more later.

Another aircraft of that year of new aircraft, 1930, is the Dornier DoX flying boat, a 'one-off' which exhibited a number of advanced and interesting cockpit features. For example, there were only two throttles on the 'bridge' for the twelve engines — six pulling and six pushing. Also there were only two rpm indicators: these displayed the mean rpm of each group of six engines. A panel of lights in the cockpit indicated which of the engines had been connected by the flight engineer to the throttle levers. Although this overcame the problem of grasping twelve throttle levers it was contrary to the accepted practice that the pilot in command must have direct control of all engines.

In his amidships station the flight engineer had a comprehensive array of controls and instruments for all twelve engines. The DoX anticipated a time when detailed management of the engines in large transport aircraft would become

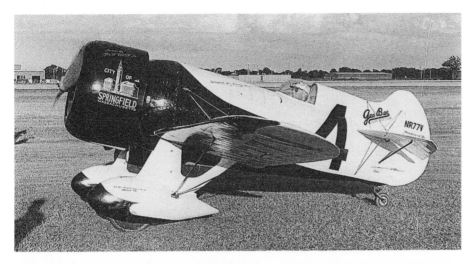

Far left *'Since we go to sea, we need a mast on which to mount a wind driven generator, two pitot heads and the forward yard for the antenna wires. Also we need a hatch for messing about with mooring cables.' Latecoere 522 flying boat.* (John Stroud)

Middle far left *Bleriot 5190 flying boat of the 1930s operating the South Atlantic routes. The narrow flight deck is housed within the wing to fuselage structure and immediately under the middle engine.* (John Stroud)

Bottom far left *The flight deck of the Dornier Do X, circa 1930. A fully equipped engineer's station reduced the number of instruments and controls in front of the pilots.* (John Stroud)

Above left *One of the Gee Bee series of racing monoplanes of the 1930s. Six experienced pilots were killed by this example of 'the smallest airframe with the biggest engine' design concept. As early as 1932 Doolittle flew one at nearly 300 mph. The cockpit was a tight fit for all but the smallest pilot.* (via Aeroplane Monthly)

Left *Pendant throttles in a Sikorsky S42 flying boat, c.1934.* (via Aeroplane Monthly)

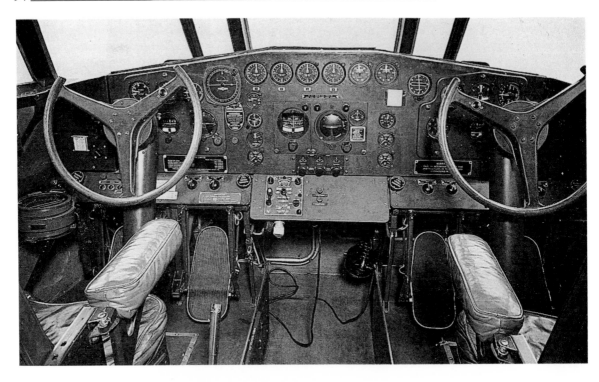

This is the version of the Boeing 314 flying boat operated by British Overseas Airways during the Second World War on the North Atlantic route; hence the P type aperiodic compass on the left and the Aldis signalling lamp stowed alongside the rudder pedals. The throttle and other engine levers are out of the picture at the outboard side of each pilot's seat. (via Aeroplane Monthly)

the responsibility of a flight engineer.

Many of the multi-engine monoplanes of this period were high-wing, a style which persisted into the 1940s with such aircraft as the Avro York and the Consolidated Catalina, both of which were used on civil routes after World War Two. As with the well known generation of Sikorsky flying boats, S42s for example, the primary engine controls were mounted under the overhead of the flight deck. There is, then, this important group of 'pendant throttle' aircraft. In this position, under the centre line of the overhead, the run of the control wires or rods was simpler than had there been a central pedestal layout. Of course, in a flying boat pendant throttles allowed a companionway forward between the two pilots to the bow position when performing nautical evolutions such as 'Let go for'd' and 'Secure to buoy'.

A notable exception to the pendant throttle arrangement was the Boeing 314, four-engine, transoceanic flying boat of 1939. The flight deck had throttle pedestals at the outboard side of both pilots.

A standard nose

From about 1930 onwards the emergence can be traced of the V-shaped, raked windscreen which is still in use. The rounded-section fuselage with lines fairing into a pointed nose became the norm, as did the low-wing monoplane multi-engine configuration. But there are always exceptions: the Handley Page 42 for example. The antiquity of the HP42 was very apparent when it stood alongside the sleeker and faster aircraft of other airlines. Nevertheless, irrespective of its dated design as an airliner, the flight deck deserves a closer look. Like the aircraft as a whole it was magnificent; particularly the very large aileron control wheels and the extensive fenestration from which the pilots surveyed the world slowly passing below. The large aileron wheels were needed to supplement the pilot's muscles when setting in motion the

The Handley Page 42 cockpit, dominated by the large aileron control wheels. The engine instruments are concentrated in front of the second pilot; excellent view forward, to the sides and upwards. (Smiths Industries)

long series of cables, cranks and pulleys which reached up, back and out to the ailerons. In contrast, the four throttle levers were small. Typical of its time, the engine instruments in the 'front office' of the HP42 were disposed in front of the second pilot. In contrast, the captain's panel had few instruments.

At one time an HP42 was equipped with a cantilever frame extending for-

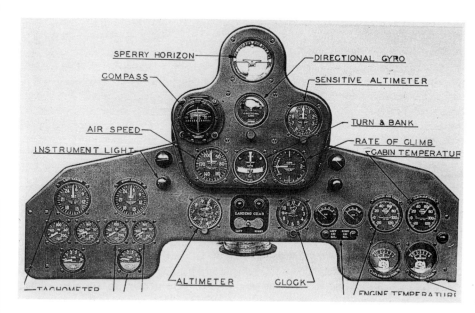

Curtiss Condor instrument panel, circa 1932, with, for its time, a comprehensive array of instruments, particularly those needed for flying at night and in poor visibility. (via Aeroplane Monthly)

Above *Dewoitine D338, a typical long-nosed French airliner of the 1930s.* (John Stroud)

Right *One disadvantage of the tri-motor, apparent in this photograph of the Wibault 282T 12, was the poor forward view when taxying due to the middle engine.* (John Stroud)

ward from the cockpit to carry a cross bar. This was installed at the request of some pilots who were finding it difficult to fly straight and level because the nose provided no frame of reference. However, there had been, and would be, many other types of aircraft without a good frame of reference, yet their pilots did not complain. Eventually the frame was removed.

The HP42 was not the only biplane airliner to enter service after 1930: among a number of types, including the DH86, was the twin-engine Curtis Condor. Its fully-enclosed cockpit had one of the earlier examples of an integrated panel of instruments. However, no attempt was made to dispose the different instruments in logical groupings on the integrated panel. For example, in front of the Captain were the rpm, oil pressure and temperature indicators and the fuel pressure gauges. In front of the second pilot were the cylinder head temperature, cabin and outside air temperature indicators as well as the contents indicators for the two fuel tanks. The centre part of the panel was a subsystem which carried the Sperry artificial horizon, compass, directional gyro, altimeter, ASI, turn and slip and vertical speed indicators. In the lower centre of the main panel was the undercarriage selection buttons and indicator light, for although it was a biplane the undercarriage was retractable.

Despite its poor ergonomics the Condor's instrument panel was both comprehensive and up to date; without it, scheduled operations in poor visibility and adverse weather conditions would not have been practicable.

At this time, the first half of the thirties, national aviation characteristics were still discernible among the cockpits of the major civil aviation countries: in order of passengers carried, the United States, Germany, France, Italy and the United Kingdom. The French had a number of tri-motor types in service in the early thirties. Some of these were notable for the

Wibault 283, with separate triple throttles for each pilot, recording rpm indicators for the three engines and other engine instruments concentrated on the centre panel. Few flight instruments, however, in front of the captain, and apparently none for the second pilot! (John Stroud)

Bloch 220, with an extensive array of flight instruments for the captain and the radio in front of the second pilot. No windscreen wipers or de-icing system, therefore the glass in front of each pilot can be slid open to give a clear view. (John Stroud)

A photograph taken circa 1912 of a Curtiss seaplane with Sperry autopilot. Note the cine camera mounted on a tripod abaft the engine. (Sperry)

long 'bonnet' ahead of the cockpit. There appeared to be some affinity with the racing and sporting cars of the time. The Dewoitine D338 was over 12 feet from propeller to the sharply raked windscreen. In contrast, the Wibault 282T had a nose dimensionally similar to that of the Ju52, but with a far more elegant and less drag-producing windscreen. The cockpit was, perhaps, typical of French design of the period. One interesting feature was the 'engine turned' patterned, shiny metal instrument panel with twelve indicators for the three 350-hp Gnome Rhone radials. With only one or two instruments in front of the captain on the left, there was more panel than instruments. Although not an unusually wide cockpit, the pilots were given individual groups of three throttle levers.

A feature of the cockpit of the Breguet 393T of 1933 were the old-fashioned carriage handles for the main fuel cocks. An early example of engine usage monitoring were the rpm indicators, each of which had a pen-on-chart automatic recorder.

The rapid replacement of tri-motors except in Germany and Italy, in the late 1930s by twin-engine, all-metal, monoplanes encouraged some standardization of the civil cockpit layout. Regularity and economy of operations finally replaced any 'press on regardless' techniques. This applied particularly to North America and Europe. Before 1935, for example, neither the North or South Atlantic was crossed by passenger aircraft operating scheduled services. As late as 1936 in air transport history Jean Mermoz and his crew disappeared in the four-engine Croix du Sud flying boat attempting to maintain a scheduled service between Africa and South America. He and that other great French pilot, Antoine de St Exupery, flew long distances, sometimes in single-engine aircraft, equipped with cockpits whose design reflected the standards of the time and therefore added to their problems of fuel conservation and navigation.

St Exupery's books on flying, even when translated from the French, are among the most descriptive of the pilot's

environment in the 1920s and 30s.

In *Wind, Sand and Stars* St Exupery vividly captures the atmosphere of flying the mails in the late 1920s through storms and poor visibility at night, '...When the skies are filled with black vapours, when fog and sand and sea are confounded in a brew in which they become indistinguishable, when gleaming flashes wheel treacherously in these skey swamps, the pilot purges himself of the phantoms at a single stroke. He lights his lamps. He brings sanity into his house, as a lonely cottage on a fearsome heath. And the crew travel a sort of submarine route in a lighted chamber.

'Pilot, mechanic and radio operator are shut up in what might be a laboratory. They are obedient to the play of dial hands, not to the unrolling landscape. Out of doors the mountains are immersed in tenebrous darkness: but they are no longer mountains, they are invisible powers whose approach must be computed.'

St Exupery is here emphasizing the need to trust one's instruments and not the often misleading phenomena seen through the cockpit windows.

Automatic pilots, which were to become a feature of many of the larger types of aircraft, were not developed as production items until after 1930. In Britain the Smith's automatic pilot, an arrangement of gyros and pneumatics, remained in use until replaced by an all-electric type. In the RAF in the Second World War many aircraft designed to have automatic pilots entered squadron service without them being fitted because of production problems. The tremendous pace of aircraft construction often outstripped the output of component suppliers. It was not an uncommon experience to enter the cockpit of a British aircraft in the 1940s to find that the autopilot 'plumbing' has been installed but not the control units. In contrast American autopilot production kept pace with new aircraft, so that pilots were not deprived of this useful adjunct to flying.

Flight deck, circa *1939, of the Lockheed Lodestar, showing twin pointer engine instruments top centre and a central controls pedestal with many more controls than the Electra and other civil aircraft of the 1930s.* (Lockheed)

CHAPTER FIVE

FLYING THE RANGE

Douglas commercial

The advent of the Douglas Commercial series, starting with the DC1 and leading on to the DC3, contributed much to the establishment of the scheduled intensive airline network of North America. The equipment and layout of the DC3 cockpit was the precursor of the flight decks of the forties and fifties. The DC3 also presaged the demise of the romantic trimotors from Fokker, Ford, Savoia Marcheti and others.

A general description will have to be used for the DC3 cockpit, as there have been hundreds of different operators in many different countries, including the USSR, each having its own ideas about the cockpit equipment.

The DC3, like many other aircraft of its time, had a Sperry autopilot as the central part of the main instrument panel, surmounted, usually, by the radio compass. Engine instruments were concentrated in front of the second pilot and with the majority of the controls on the central pedestal. The DC3 cockpit was well equipped with radio aids and with engine instruments but none of these was arranged in any particular order. The flight instruments, apart from those on the Sperry panel, were also in no particular order and therefore, in this respect, were as in other American types.

This lack of a logical arrangement was highlighted when pilots had to execute holding patterns and approaches in the overloaded terminal areas of the northeast corridor of the USA. This was in the first few years after the end of the Second World War, when commercial air traffic increased out of all expectation and instrument flying fatigue became a serious problem.

What are not usually shown in an illustration of the DC3 cockpit are the headphones for each pilot. These were important items of cockpit equipment because the primary navigation aid was the radio-range. Through their headphones the pilots listened and responded to the 'dot-dash' to the left and the 'dash-dot' to the right sequences of the radio ranges which by the end of the 1930s provided a network covering the whole of the USA.

A review of multi-engined civil aircraft flight decks during the early 1930s highlights three basic allocations of main instrument panel space:

(a) flight instruments and autopilot in the centre with engine instruments to the right and only a clock in front of the captain

(b) flight instrumentation on the left, autopilot in the centre and engine instruments on the right

(c) two sets of flight instruments, with

DC2 : the principal flight instruments arranged in a row below the Sperry autopilot panel; a Sperry artificial horizon set above the manifold pressure; and rpm indicators in front of the left-hand seat. Access to the seats is facilitated by the inverted-L shape of the control columns which are mounted outboard of the seats. (Smiths Industries)

Stinson Model A, circa 1931, with a reverse rake windscreen. (via Aeroplane Monthly)

autopilot and engine instruments in the centre of the panel.

Each of these basic arrangements reflected both the complexity of the aircraft type and the particular operator's ideas about the respective duties of each crew member.

The technological impact and resulting proliferation of the DC2 and 3 on world commercial routes is an important part of aviation history. Part of the Douglas story is concerned with a cockpit layout which became archetypal of two-pilot civil operation. Another stereotype feature was the design of the flight deck windows, which, possibly more than any other part of the design, became a Douglas trademark.

Although the stepped windscreen of the DC2/DC3 family set the standard which was to follow, there were a number of aircraft types with reverse raked windscreens. This was done to avoid reflections from the cockpit lights.

Both the Boeing 307 Stratoliner four-engine, pressurized airliner and the elegant Curtiss-Wright CW–20 had nose shapes which anticipated those of jet aircraft. The Stratoliner flight deck was described at the time as an instrument panel with a slot across the middle for the pilots to see through.

The CW–20 had a flight deck with layout, controls and instruments along with a cabin finish which was much in advance of its time, and it also included an illuminated checklist on which the pilot could select the appropriate flight mode, such as take-off or landing. The state of the different systems needed for this phase of the flight would then be indicated on this panel.

It almost goes without saying that a basic check list in all aircraft was provided by mnemonics. For example, HTMPFG, which in a piston-engine aircraft referred to Hydraulics, Throttle friction, Mixture, Propeller pitch, Flaps and Fuel cocks and engine-cooling Gills. Such mnemonics ensured, among other things, that the throttles would not vibrate back from the take-off power position, that the propellers were in fine pitch and that the flaps were set for take-off.

During the 1930s there was a tendency

Boeing 307 Stratoliner, circa 1939, one of the first production standard pressurized transport aircraft. The windscreen frames do not break the continuity of the forward lines of the fuselage. (via Aeroplane Monthly)

Far left *Curtiss Wright CW 20, circa 1940. The flight deck windows are faired into the shapely nose, and the design of the controls and instruments set a new standard. (via Aeroplane Monthly)*

Left *Illuminated checklist in a CW 20: by selecting the flight mode, such as START, the crew were presented with a sequenced and illuminated set of indications for each item in the list. (via Aeroplane Monthly)*

Above *This British 1930s flying boat, believed to be a Short Scion with Captain O. P. Jones in command, has a purely functional flight deck with the throttle pedestal partly behind the first pilot's right elbow.* (via Aeroplane Monthly)

Above right *Junkers 86, circa 1934, another example of German attention to the overall design and finish of a cockpit. The right-hand seat position had no flight controls and was used*

in American flight deck designs, particularly for small twins, to produce cockpits and their fittings so as to imitate the sumptuous interiors of the contemporary automobile. About this time there was even the suggestion that the different aircraft configurations for take-off, climb, cruise, descent and landing should be selectable not with individual levers but through a common control analogous to the gear shift on a car. For a number of reasons, not the least of which was safety, that idea was not pursued. During the late 1930s and early 1940s the aeroplane in North America was often a target for the industrial designer — who at that time was obsessed with streamlining everything from toothbrushes to battleships. Although this kind of attention was sometimes successful in tidying up

the flight deck, by providing elegantly designed panels of dials and selectors, the ergonomics of a layout were often ignored.

Between 1930 and 1950 the multiple piston-engined, low wing, monoplane with pressurized hull evolved from the biplane. The various advances that took place included the introduction of the retractable undercarriage, flaps, automatic pilot, and constant-speed and reversing propellers, and there was a significant increase in the number of controls and instruments on the flight deck. No longer were engine instruments outside the cockpit and, apart from a pair of headphones, pilots no longer had to wear any special equipment or clothing. By the end of the era, air transport had become an accepted facet of the post-war world and its rapid growth was to lead to successive generations of new transport aircraft with ever more complex 'front offices'. The time was now ripe for the ergonomics expert to display his skills, while the number and qualifications of the occupants of the flight deck became matters of pressing importance.

From the mid-1930s increasing use was made of variable position engine cowling gills. These introduced an additional control as well as an additional problem for the pilot. Namely, adjusting the degree of gill opening to limit cylinder head temperature, yet, at the same time, avoiding a vicious circle of gills open and increased drag, which in turn required more engine power and therefore higher temperatures ... and so on.

Cockpits in general became more complex as controls and instruments proliferated. Unfortunately little was known about the adverse effects of badly positioned controls and illogically arranged panels of instruments. Many civil cockpits, like their air force counterparts, gave the impression that their designer had used the blindfold party game of 'sticking the tail on the donkey' technique. One particular assumption on the part of a design office was that all pilots had three hands and eyes in their elbows.

by the radio operator. Because the Ju 86 was designed for use either as a passenger transport or as a bomber, a second set of controls was not fitted so as to leave a gangway forward to a bomb aimer's position in the nose. (John Stroud)

Below *The evolution of the civil flight deck, 1920–45.* (Author)

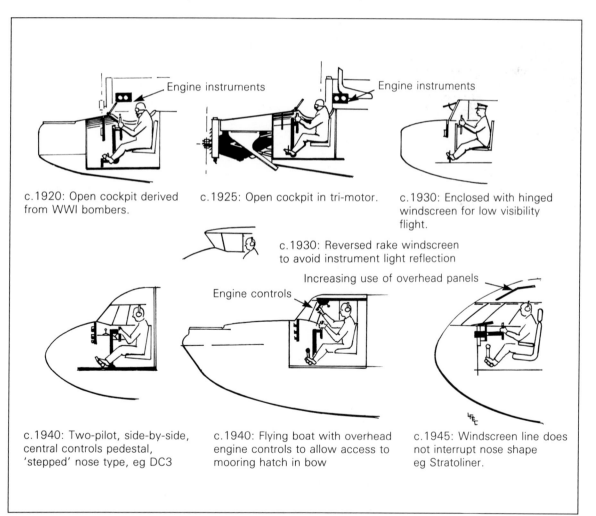

c.1920: Open cockpit derived from WWI bombers.

c.1925: Open cockpit in tri-motor.

c.1930: Enclosed with hinged windscreen for low visibility flight.

c.1930: Reversed rake windscreen to avoid instrument light reflection

Increasing use of overhead panels

Engine controls

c.1940: Two-pilot, side-by-side, central controls pedestal, 'stepped' nose type, eg DC3

c.1940: Flying boat with overhead engine controls to allow access to mooring hatch in bow

c.1945: Windscreen line does not interrupt nose shape eg Stratoliner.

B & V Ha 139 float plane. A crew of two pilots, navigator, radio operator and flight engineer are crowded into the flight deck area. Two of these aircraft were evaluated for transatlantic services in 1937 operating from the catapult-equipped depot ship Schwabenland. *(John Stroud)*

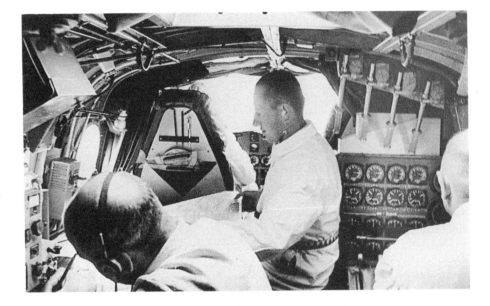

Cockpit of Mercury, the upper mail plane component of the Mercury/Maia of 1938. A British-type aperiodic compass is installed inverted on the overhead of the cockpit with a hinged viewing mirror. The mail-carrying Mercury was borne aloft by the larger Miai, then, on release, D.C.T. Bennett (later Air Vice Marshal in the RAF's Pathfinder Force) and A.J. Coster flew the aircraft to Montreal, a flight of over 20 hours. (via Aeroplane Monthly)

Two-pilot crews

Except in the smaller civil aircraft the two-pilot crew became standard from about 1935 onwards. The second member of the crew had not necessarily been a pilot and even if qualified spent most of the time as wireless operator, flight engineer and cabin attendant. As an example of second pilot status a contemporary description of the AW Atalanta, 1932, said: '...those [instruments] which require constant observation are placed at the port (*sic*) end under the eyes of the chief pilot while those which need less frequent reading are in front ... of the second pilot.' In some ways an inaccurate comment because it suggests that the engine instruments did not require frequent reading, which in 1932 was not the case. Many civil airline pilots acquired from long experience the special skill of a one-man band. Some were acutely conscious of their ability and resented any help. As already mentioned, some did all the piloting and navigating — including letting down at the destination by visual contact with familiar landmarks close to the airfield.

For long-range navigation, dead-reckoning (i.e. deduced reckoning-DR) and, if a navigator available, sextant 'shots' of sun or stars were the usual methods of fixing an aircraft's position. Commercial flights were undertaken on routes which traversed mountains whose tops were above an aircraft's maximum operating height. Sometimes headwinds were encountered which resulted in ground speeds so low that, figuratively, the passengers could get out and walk. Except in the USA, with its increasing use of the radio range in the 1930s, reliance was placed on ground-based radio direction finding systems which used transmissions from an aircraft to plot its position.

The 'Basic Six'

In 1937 the RAF settled on six essential flight instruments in a logical grouping which would remain the standard blind-flying panel for the next 20 years. The new RAF 'Basic Six' panel consisted of: airspeed indicator, gyro horizon, vertical speed indicator, altimeter, directional gyro, and turn and bank indicator. The RAF 'Basic Six' concept carried over into civil aviation, but after the Second World War the arrangement of instruments was changed in favour of airspeed, artificial horizon and altimeter in the top row, and radio compass, direction indicator and vertical speed in the bottom row.

With the DH91 Albatross, of renowned beauty of line, British cockpit design took a step forward. The primary 'instrument flight' panel was placed directly in front of the first pilot. It was made up of two rows of three instruments: top-airspeed, gyro horizon, vertical speed, bottom-altimeter, gyro heading, turn and slip. To be able to write about 'rows' of instruments instead of a 'scattering' was a step in the right direction. As was fashionable at the time, many secondary instruments were placed on a sloping shelf across the bottom of the main panel. The six primary flight instruments reflected the growing influence of the RAF Basic Six panel, from which was evolved some 15 years later the Basic T layout for civil aircraft. In this important respect British cockpit design remained in advance of the rest of the world for many years.

This method of improving the pilot's instrument scan was not followed by other countries. In the USA, for example, aircraft were built over the next 15 years which had far less satisfactory arrangements of the instruments. As late as 1947 eye movement records made of pilots scanning a typical panel highlighted the fact that the instruments had not been arranged in accordance with relative frequency of use, let alone importance.

The vertical speed indicator was usually termed 'rate of climb', presumably because in those days there was not much problem in going 'downhill', but rates of going 'uphill' were rather slow compared with later jet air-

An elegant nose and
shapely windscreen
characterized the DH
91 Frobisher, seen
with passengers
boarding in front of
the control tower at
Croydon, London's
principal airport in the
1930s. Until the early
1950s many airliners
flew national ensigns
and company house
flags so as to emulate
the departure and
arrival of ships. This
British civil aviation
ensign would have
been retracted once
the aircraft started to
move. (British
Airways)

Basic Six panel of
flight instruments in a
Sea Gladiator, as
operated by the RAF
in the defence of
Malta in the Second
World War. Above
the instrument panel is
the cross tube which
supports the reflector
gun sight. Although
this is the cockpit of a
biplane fighter, much
of the equipment is
typical of British
monoplane fighters of
the early 1940s.
(Shuttleworth
Collection)

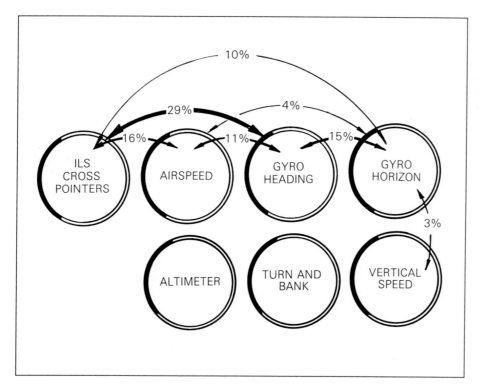

Eye movements during an ILS approach, circa 1950, using a pre-1950 American non-basic T arrangement of the principal instruments. (Author)

craft performance.

Much has been recorded about the difficulties of locating controls in the dark and having to operate more than two levers or switches simultaneously. Although this situation was certainly often encountered, pilots learned to cope with it. It was only when an emergency occurred, and the pilot's workload suddenly increased well above the normal, that the dangers of a badly arranged flight deck and its equipment became significant.

Money and safety

A fundamental factor in the relationship between civil pilots and the design of aircraft in the 1930s and to some extent in the 1950s was that of the employment situation in aviation. This was, of course, little different from the 1920s. Pilots who had chosen a career in civil aviation from a love of flying nevertheless had to earn a living, so they were never in too great a hurry to complain about the design of the cockpit. Even though the pilot profession may have appeared glamorous to those not flying aeroplanes, those who did fly often received low salaries and had poor job security. This was the result of the financial situation of many operators in the thirties who had to depend on the faith in aviation of those who supplied the money. Civil aviation was still a long way from becoming both an acceptable and unquestioned method of transport. The inevitable accidents were given banner headlines in the press.

Although by 1938 there had been many advances in aviation, in general few pilots had sufficient experience of flying on instruments or were skilled at it. Both civil and air force pilots usually chose to try and fly under the overcast rather than attempt a climb on top and then face an instrument descent through cloud for a landing. In this year, in Britain alone, despite technical achievements there were many accidents resulting from trying to continue a flight in deteriorating visibility.

The flight engineer's station in a Boeing 314 flying boat. This typifies the attention paid by American designers to the finish of a flight deck, with its soundproofing lining and neatly arranged control desks for radio operator (foreground) and engineer. This particular B 314 was operated by British Overseas Airways during the Second World War on the North Atlantic route. (via Aeroplane Monthly)

Perhaps the most significant change in instrumentation by the mid-1930s was the concentration of all engine indicators in front of the pilots or on a separate flight engineer's panel. As mentioned, earlier practice inherited from First World War bomber design placed some instruments on the inboard sides of the engine nacelles. Reliable remote-reading instrument systems took some years to develop.

The crews of tri-motors usually had the benefit of cockpit instruments for the middle engine. But at night many continued to point a torch (flashlight) at the small nacelle-mounted instrument panel in order to try and check on the health of an outboard engine.

The advent of four-engine machines tended to put an end to nacelle-mounted instruments: hence the array of engine instruments in front of the second pilot of an H42. No doubt someone in the drawing office at Handley Page, Cricklewood, had been instructed to devise a way of avoiding the cost of remote-reading engine instruments. Nevertheless, with two of the engines well above the pilots' heads, it would have been stretching things too far to have fitted instruments to the underside of the nacelles.

In the era of pounding pistons, short exhaust pipes and thin-walled cabins there were more than enough decibels and heterodyning beats assailing the passengers' ears. An instrument for synchronizing the engines was not available in the 1930s. Thus in the Ju52, for example, a small mirror was fitted on the inboard side of each engine nacelle of some aircraft so that the pilots could simultaneously see the propellers of two engines. The reflections in the mirror were used in the manner of a stroboscope to adjust the rpm of an outboard motor to match that of the middle engine. In four-engine aircraft it was sometimes possible to use the stroboscopic technique between adjacent propellers. Eventually instruments for synchronizing engines were introduced.

The neatly arranged cockpit of the Dornier Do 26 four-engine flying boat, circa 1938. The rudder pedals were of an unusual design operating in slide boxes; the two wheels under the overhead were for trimming the ailerons and elevator; and both pilots were provided with a full set of flight instruments. The small door in the bulkhead below the throttles pedestal gave access to the bow position. (via Aeroplane Monthly)

The Do 26 flight engineer's station. The instruments were arranged to match the 'two pulling and two pushing' configuration of the engines. (via Aeroplane Monthly)

CHAPTER SIX

AIR WAR COCKPITS

Engine control

The rapid re-equipment of air forces from 1934 onwards with all-metal monoplane fighters and bombers also brought significant changes to the look of the cockpit and its equipment. The increasing use of engines having variable pitch propellers and wings with variable flaps as well as retractable undercarriages added to the number of controls.

Engine handling still remained an important part of the pilot's task. The piston engines of the 1930s had to be operated with care to prevent in-flight failure. In Britain, automatic boost and mixture controls were developed before war broke out, and by 1940 RAF fighters were also fitted with contant-speed propellers. These automatic systems enabled a pilot to concentrate on the target without having to worry about over-speeding or over-boosting the engine. In contrast, the majority of American aircraft at that time did not have engines fitted with automatic boost controls — which meant that their pilots had to keep an eye on the manifold pressure (boost) indicator whenever making large throttle changes.

During the late 1930s and 40s national aircraft characteristics could be identified among the cockpits of French, German, Italian, American and British aircraft.

Even blindfolded a pilot could feel and smell the differences. In the French and Italian aircraft, of course, the throttle movement of pull to increase power was very different from the standard adopted by other nations. French aircraft which escaped to the Allies in 1940 and those intercepted on their way from American factories to France had to have their throttle linkages changed to conform to the accepted direction of movement. However, before all were converted, a number of accidents resulted when non-French pilots flew DB7s (Bostons), Curtiss Hawk 75As and others.

A similar problem occurred later in the war when Italian aircraft fell into other hands. Fortunately by the end of 1943 the majority of Italian aircraft — Italy by then having changed sides — were flown by Italian pilots who continued to pull open the throttle like engine drivers to increase power. After the war, both the French and Italian aircraft industries took some time to re-establish and therefore when starting with a 'clean sheet of paper' they arranged the throttles to conform with the rest of the world.

The overall state of cockpit development among the principal aviation nations, Russia excepted because of lack of information, can be summarized as follows. In American aircraft, cockpits were distinguished by the greater number of switches because of the extensive use of electric motors and actuators and the apparent lack of any consistent and logical arrangement of the instruments. Yet the American cockpit of this era was far more comfortable than those of the majority of aircraft in other countries.

British cockpit design practice from 1936 onwards for air force aircraft continued to exhibit a wide divergence of ideas among the different constructors and, in general, with little consideration for the comfort of the pilot. There was a degree of uniformity, in that the majority of RAF aircraft types were fitted with a standard blind flying panel of the six essential instruments of speed, attitude, vertical speed, height and turn and slip.

German cockpits of this period reflected the attention paid to detail and to the design and finish of accessories which characterized the products of Junkers, Heinkel, Messerschmidt and others. In contrast to, say, British designs, an instrument would be mounted on a carefully shaped and finished bracket and all wiring neatly confined to conduits.

Another important feature of German multi-engine aircraft was the extensive fenestration which afforded the pilot wide arcs-of-vision. This reflected the original role of the Luftwaffe as an air force intended primarily as the spearhead of the army. The ability to see between one's feet prior to starting a dive-bombing attack was an important design requirement.

French cockpits prior to 1940, as far as design for the benefit of the pilot is concerned, in general fell somewhere between British and German ideas. Unfortunately between the declaration of war and the German Blitzkrieg, the French air force had only six months in which to perfect detail design of cockpits in accordance with operational needs. Even the best aircraft types were few in number because of the chaotic state of the aircraft industry during the late 1930s. The pilots and others in the Armée de l'Air were confident, well trained and determined,

Breguet 693 twin-engine attack/bomber of the French air force, circa 1940. The throttle levers, close to the trimming wheel, are in the fully forward position which, until the end of the Second World War, was the closed position in French and Italian aircraft. (via Aeroplane Monthly)

The reflector gunsight in the cockpit of a Spitfire. At the base of the sight can be seen the knurled rings by which the pilot set target wingspan and range. (via Aeroplane Monthly)

but were let down by an industry which failed to put excellent ideas into production.

Reflector gunsights

Just as the ring and bead and optical sights, such as the Aldis, had formed an important part of the cockpit furniture, albeit outside, so did the reflector gunsights which came into use in the late 1930s. Very few illustrations exist of the reflector sights prior to about 1940 because of censorship. Even official publications, such as *Pilot's Notes*, usually omitted the gunsight.

When General Milch of the Luftwaffe visited RAF Hornchurch in October 1937, attempts were made to prevent him looking too closely at the reflector gunsights in the Gladiator fighters. Presumably not because he was unaware

of this particular sighting system but because the range adjustment scale was marked He111, Ju88, Do18 etc.

The RAF's two front-line fighters at the beginning of the Second World War came from different stables, yet both had cockpits in which the controls and ancillary instruments and levers were disposed in accordance with the needs of the installation engineer — and therefore not always in accord with what suited the pilot. Coming from the Miles Master or the NA Harvard the new pilot exchanged the orderly array of cockpit equipment, particularly that of the Master, for the two-handed confusion of the Hurricane and the Spitfire. The undercarriage of the MK.1 Spitfire had to be manually pumped up after take-off, using a lever at the pilot's right hand side. In the Hurricane, should the hydraulic system fail to lower the wheels, the pilot could release the up-locks with his feet. That pilots coped in these ambidextrous cockpits is a credit to the high standard of training, and to the adaptability of man to the strange and the awkward.

A significant cockpit difference between the two fighters was in the canopies. The Hurricane's was made up of a number of separate panels, whereas the Spitfire design team took advantage of the latest techniques in moulded Perspex. Another difference was the small drop-down door on the side of the Spitfire, which improved access.

Unlike its opponent, the Messerschmitt Bf109, the Spitfire did not retain its close-fitting canopy for long. Test pilot Jeffrey Quill, in his book on flying the Spitfire, recounts the battle he had to have improvements made to the cockpit canopy and windscreen. The forward side panels were of curved plastic which distorted the pilot's view, and the canopy prevented the pilot turning his head sufficiently to see astern. The test of war prompted two major changes to the shape of the canopy before the advent of the bubble canopy on the final version. In contrast the Hurricane went right through the war with only minor changes to its much-fenestrated canopy.

A familiar feature to many Spitfire pilots was the small red ball which hung just above their foreheads. When this was pulled it actuated a series of plungers which freed the canopy from the runners so that the airstream carried it clear of the aircraft. This modification, devised by Martin Baker, was introduced following operational experience in which some pilots had found that baling out was hampered by trying to slide back the canopy.

A comment by a pilot on lowering himself into the cockpit of a Spitfire XIV: 'The layout, though similar to that on earlier marks, has been more seriously organized to deal with all the extras which have been piled on to the Spitfire during the war. In the Mk.XIV the radiator flap and automatic blower-

change test buttons, oil dilution button, fuel booster pump, navigation lights and other switches are arranged in a neat row on the left.' A 'neat row' was an unusual feature of a British aircraft of that generation.

The five-bladed propeller of the Griffon engine rotated anti-clockwise, viewed from the cockpit, so that on take-off the aircraft tended to swing to the right: 'Merlin' Spitfires swung to the left. Because of the Griffon engine's bulk, compared with that of the Merlin, the pilot's forward view during taxying and on the approach to land was even more restricted than before. However, most Spitfire pilots, irrespective of mark, held

The cockpit of an early version of the Spitfire in which the pilot had to change hands on the control column to use his right hand on the large black hydraulic pump handle to raise the undercarriage. The mounting for a reflector gun sight is occupied by a ring and bead sight. This Spitfire does not have the two-position anti-G pedals of later versions. (Vickers)

Right *Later version of the Spitfire; the under-carriage hand pump has been replaced by a selector lever for the hydraulic system and anti-G two-level pedals installed. The P-type aperiodic compass is in the traditional British, difficult to read, position in front of the stick.* (British Aerospace)

Below *Hawker Typhoon, circa 1941: Basic Six panel; bilges in full view; gun trigger button and brake lever on circular grip of control column; compass between pilot's feet; engine instruments on the right.* (British Aerospace)

a continuous curved approach so that the intended landing spot was in view for as long as possible.

Perhaps one of the most distinguishing features of RAF cockpits was the large magnetic compass which was often mounted between the pilot's feet, and which was therefore partly obscured by the control column.

Opposing the Spitfire and Hurricane of RAF Fighter Command in 1940 was the Bf109. The cockpit of the German premier fighter was very different from those of its rivals. Compared with the two British fighters the Bf109 cockpit was very cramped and with a canopy which provided little headroom — although it did incorporate part of the pilot's protective armour plate which formed the seat. However, Luftwaffe pilots were reported as finding the controls and instruments satisfactory.

The 1940 version of the Bf109 had a very different arrangement from the RAF Basic Six of the primary flight instruments. From left to right, starting top left, in two rows of three they were: altimeter, magnetic compass, boost gauge, airspeed indicator, turn and slip and rpm indicator. The ignition switches were arranged in what might be termed the 'German-American'. In place of the individual switches of British cockpits there was one lever moving in a quadrant. The pilot could select BOTH OFF, M1, M2 or M1 plus M2: M meaning Magneto. Not to be found in British or American cockpits of that era was the propeller pitch indicator of the Bf109, which in the earlier versions did not have a constant-speed propeller.

Taxying the long-nosed fighters of the 1940s required frequent changes of direction in order to see ahead. In the Bf109 this problem was aggravated by the need to keep the canopy, which hinged up to the right, closed. The Bell Aircobra, engine amidships fighter, had a car-type door on the right and, as with the 'car door' of the Typhoon and the Bf109's canopy, this had to be closed for taxying.

The Typhoon cockpit marked a significant departure from previous RAF cockpit design. Instead of a sliding canopy, as on the Spitfire for example, access was through a door on the right-hand side and with a lifting section above the pilot's head — a layout similar to that of the Bell Airacobra. Later versions of this successor to the Hurricane were fitted with one-piece moulded Perspex canopies which could be slid back along the top of the fuselage.

The pilot sat immediately behind the massive engine of the Typhoon, whereas in the Tempest the engine was positioned further forward to make room for a

Cockpit of a Bf 109 of the German air force, circa 1940. The Revi reflector sight was less bulky than those used by the RAF, and the ignition control (left on panel) was of the American multi-position type. The canopy hinged up to the right and therefore had to be closed when taxying. Note the absence of a vertical speed indicator. (via Aeroplane Monthly)

A German communications and trainer twin-engine aircraft, the Focke-Wulf Fw 58. (via Aeroplane Monthly)

fuselage fuel tank. The Tempest's cockpit, equipment and canopy were similar to those for the later versions of the Typhoon.

At this stage of the war the lead-computing gyro gunsight was becoming a significant feature of RAF cockpits. Very much larger than the fixed reticle reflector sight, the gyro sight filled most of the space between the windscreen pillars. This improved method of aiming guns and rockets introduced a significant change to the shape of the throttle lever, which now had to incorporate a twist grip with which the pilot operated the target-ranging system of the sight.

The sight mounting bar in the Tempest conveniently provided a suitable hand-grip when getting in and out of the seat. Unfortunately, constant use began to distort the mounting, so throwing the sight out of alignment. Some versions of the Tempest did not have the familiar

combining glass on the gunsight; the collimated images of the optical system were reflected directly off the windscreen. This arrangement had both advantages and disadvantages. It certainly improved the pilot's forward view, but as the airspeed varied so did the shape of the windscreen, and this tended to throw the sight out of correct alignment.

A contemporary comment on flying the Tempest made some criticisms of the cockpit and its equipment — criticisms which were shared with a number of other aircraft types: 'As in the Hurricane and Typhoon, there is no floor to the cockpit as such, but the splayed heel-trays run from the seat to each of the rudder pedals, and the only inconvenience of not having a floor is in dust, draughts, and the possibility of accidentally dropping something... Cockpit is, on the whole, good, and in accord with British practice, but there are one or two points worthy of criticism. With the seat adjusted for normal height the boost gauge cannot easily be seen. It would be better placed below the rpm indicator instead of to the right of it. The rudder trim control is unhandy and difficult to reach except with the finger tips, expecially when gloved... The undercarriage control lever on the port sloping panel is almost continually in contact with the calf of the leg and to avoid constant bruising and vibration the pilot has to sit rather knock-kneed... With the compass located beneath the flight instruments in the centre of the panel, view of it is completely masked by the control column, and to see the instrument either the head must be craned forward or the stick pulled back.'

With the problem of the pilot's obscured view of the compass in mind, the designers of the Reid & Sigrist Desford c.1945 reshaped the control column as a question mark.

The Tempest had a one-piece canopy sliding on rails. The hood could be jettisoned in an emergency. However, there were no means of releasing the canopy from outside the aircraft in order to rescue an unconscious pilot.

Which knob?

Some commanding officers insisted, others did not, that their crews should take every opportunity to sit in their cockpits blindfold. They had to memorize the position and become familiar with the shape of every lever, switch, knob and wheel. Many a pilot contemplating a relaxed afternoon with a good or bad book, because operations had been 'scrubbed', would be roused and driven to his dispersed aircraft out on some windswept or fogbound corner of the airfield. There he had to sit in full flying gear, blindfold, repeatedly going through all the cockpit drills.

Many pilots did not have to be ordered to do familiarization drill. Those that did so increased their chances of survival because they could overcome the bad, or

lack of, ergonomic design of their cockpit. British aircraft may have appeared old-fashioned compared with American cockpit equipment and controls. But in the dark, in smoke, or blinded by the glare of searchlights, it was sometimes easier to distinguish a bomb door lever from the flap lever when each was a fist-sized lever and not just one small switch in a row of similar switches, with which many American aircraft were equipped.

Perhaps the most vivid recollection of the Anson cockpit or flight deck or, even more correctly, the front end of the cabin, was the sociable seating arrangement. The pilot's seat up front on the left was not separated from the other occupants of the aircraft. In some ways the Anson pilot, particularly on transport flights, went about his task as if he were driving a country bus to market. Of course, this arrangement benefited the pilot when it came to raising the undercarriage of the early marks of Anson — the pilot could survey his passengers and select the one who either exhibited the most stamina or who was 'mad keen on aeroplanes' to manually crank up the gear: 140 turns.

The entrance door into the cabin of the Anson was on the right, though in the aircraft's declining years, after many facelifts, the door was moved to the more expected side: the left.

Among a number of interesting control details were the ignition switches mounted high on the centre frame of the windshield, and the ring of the 'one-gun' sight which hinged upward when not in use.

As might be expected, considering the era in which the Wellington was designed, the aircraft had some controls and instruments positioned away from the cockpit. For example, the fuel gauges were on a panel closer to the wireless operator than to the pilot. The pilot could check these gauges only by craning round to the right. Near the end of a long flight, when fuel was at a premium, the fuel gauge selector button would be sur-

The infamous '140 turns' undercarriage handle of the Anson, circa 1940, can be seen projecting on the right of the central controls pedestal. (via Aeroplane Monthly)

A Wellington bomber cockpit, circa 1939, dual control trainer version. The finger-operated brake levers were only fitted on the left-hand spectacles. The right-hand small lever just above the aperiodic compass controlled the flaps. This had to be used with care, in conjunction with the equally small indicator on the panel above, to avoid over-extending or retracting the flaps at the wrong time. The identical under-carriage lever alongside the flap lever had to be pulled to operate it to avoid confusion in the dark with the latter which had to be pushed in to be released. The two hand cranks visible in front of the control wheel manually operated the cowling gills of the radial air-cooled engines. (via Aeroplane Monthly)

reptitiously pressed by the anxious wireless operator or even by the navigator. Peripheral vision being very acute, the pilot was usually made aware of his crew's concern.

Some versions of the Wellington had emergency reserve fuel tanks in the characteristic hump of each engine nacelle. The contents of these tanks could be brought 'on line' through cocks operated by pull wires running through the wings and terminating as two rings at each side of the fuselage where the main spar passed through. On one occassion, a Wellington near the end of a long sortie from Malta out to the far reaches of the Mediterranean was struggling back through an intense storm, between raging sea and lowering cloud, and with the fuel gauge needles on the 'stops'. The second pilot was ordered aft to select the reserve tanks. After what seemed a very long time the captain felt a hand on his arm. The second pilot stood holding up the pull rings for one of the tanks, the wires having parted from the nacelle cock: 'That's sixty gallons we're not going to get,' he said.

The four main tanks plus two long-range tanks, if fitted, were interconnected by a complex of pipes and cocks festooning the main spar abaft the navigator's station. At night, with frozen fingers and by the light of a torch, a crew member would be instructed to switch on main tanks and switch off long-range tanks, or make some other arrangement of the system. Meanwhile, up front, the pilot prayed that the roar of the engines would continue unabated.

The new generation of Second World War multi-engined aircraft such as the Blenheim, Beaufort and Beaufighter for the RAF, introduced handling problems which, although present in earlier types of aircraft, were made worse by higher wing loadings and safety speeds and the difficulty, if not impossibility, of trimming out asymmetric thrust in the event of an engine failure at a critical point on take-off.

It is a characteristic of man in control of machines, not just aircraft, that with practice, and especially with experience,

Beaufighter cockpit, circa 1944: Bristol-type aileron 'wheel' spectacle with gun button and thumb-operated brake lever. The engine controls are on a pedestal to the left, the engine instruments concentrated on the lower part of the main instrument panel. The reflector gun sight can be seen (top right) swung to one side when not in use. The small indicator with two vertical bars and a U (left of the Basic Six) is a radar display. The aperiodic compass is located not between the pilot's feet but alongside on the right. (Crown Copyright)

Left-hand-on-throttles cockpit — the Handley Page Hampden, circa *1939. The brass domed domestic light switch lingered on in the Hampden well into the Second World War. The ignition switches, close to the bottom left-hand corner of the Basic Six, are interconnected with the undercarriage selector by means of a simple lever to prevent incorrect operation.* (via Aeroplane Monthly)

he is able to overcome the difficulties placed in his way both by the responses of the machine and by its designer. After a reasonable number of practice flights or, as with some aircraft types, numerous real engine failures on take-off, the pilot is able to change hands from one set of controls to another and is able to grope for and operate controls located remotely and awkwardly. And all within the few seconds available between an engine failing and the aircraft climbing away safely. H.A. Taylor, an unassuming and most experienced test and ferry pilot, summed up the relationship between aircraft handling in an emergency and cockpit design when he wrote, 'Given time, one could learn to tolerate and even to like almost any aeroplane of the World War Two period, whatever its faults and peculiarities.'

Experience of aircraft handling was one of the factors which obviously contributed to the 'survivability' chances of a wartime pilot. With each hour of ex-

perience, both of his aircraft and of avoiding trouble from the enemy and the weather, the greater became the chances of surviving an operational tour. When a pilot was new to a squadron, to the aircraft type and to the operational hazards, his survival chances were small. One badly positioned control lever, an engine failure during take-off, at night, and with a full load, and the first operational sortie ended in disaster; or at least in a bent aeroplane and a badly shaken crew.

Pilots of the RAF multi-engined aircraft had to cope with switching from cockpits which were 'left hand on throttle and right on wheel' to the opposite arrangement. Wellington, Blenheim, Beaufighter and Mosquito were among the left-hand throttle types; Whitley, Albemarle, Beaufort, Anson, Botha, Lancaster, Halifax, Liberator, B–17 and the Oxford, on which they most likely trained, had right-hand throttles. In the USAAF the majority of multi-engine aircraft types had a central throttle pedestal.

Contemporary German aircraft usually had left-hand operated throttles.

An RAF pilot might learn basic flying in a Tiger Moth or Magister with his left hand on the throttle. He might then progress to an Oxford and learn to fly with his right hand on the throttles. At an OTU he would meet an operational aircraft type such as a Beaufighter, with left-hand throttles. Pilots had to be, to say the least, ambidextrous.

The majority of British aircraft types of the Second World War had been designed before the war and each design centre had its own ideas about cockpit layout. There was little standardization, and for each type a pilot had to study the *Pilot's Notes* very carefully, because of the wide variation in the position of both primary and secondary controls.

Many papers were written by serving pilots pointing out the dangers from poor cockpit layout and from the lack of standardization. Apart from the RAF Basic Six instrument panel there was little resemblance between the cockpits of, say, a Wellington and a Blenheim, or an Oxford and a Beaufighter. Even between aircraft types from the same design stable there were differences, e.g. between Blenheim and Beaufort.

Some pilots proposed that there should be interlocks between those controls which might be confused or selected in the wrong sequence. However, interlocks were usually rejected by designers because they might add to the complication of systems and to the number of things which could go wrong. Similarly appeals for switches, instruments and levers to be arranged in a logical and consistent arrangement common to all aircraft types went unheeded.

A typical comment was, 'Lack of a uniform and rational system of cockpit layout in modern aircraft (sic c.1945) has added an unnecessary complication to flying in general and, in particular, to

A. W. Albermarle, circa 1941. The keen-eyed reader will have noticed that the vertical speed indicator has been put in the spot normally reserved for the airspeed indicator. A second set of controls can be seen stowed on the right, with two rudder pedals hinged upright on either side of the door through to the nose position. Typical gangway on the right layout. (via Aeroplane Monthly)

An RAF pilot in about 1943 wearing an oxygen mask, Mae West inflatable flotation jacket and parachute harness with a Sutton harness over the lot and secured by a quick release spring clip. (via Aeroplane Monthly)

time in which to refine cockpit design. Designers were also working against the clock to prove and install modifications. Therefore if a new switch, for example, was needed for some added system, then as long as it was within reach of the pilot, even if he had to stretch and grope, it might be located in any available space.

A test pilot's primary set of tasks concerned the verification of an aircraft's handling characteristics, i.e. is it stable? Will it meet civil or air force take-off and landing distances? His secondary task usually covered verification that the 'paper' performance of the aircraft could be achieved. Further down the list came the cockpit and its equipment. Any changes to the shape or position of a lever or the position of an instrument usually had to wait until any handling or performance deficiencies had been rectified. However, the test-pilots of the A&AEE at RAF Martlesham Heath (from 1939 at Boscombe Down) paid more attention to cockpit details.

Extensive studies into the relationship between man and machine — in other words, ergonomics, or human factors research — lay in the future. Irrespective of the goodwill of all concerned towards the average commercial or air force pilot it is a fact of aviation history that cockpit design remained low on the priority list during the evolution of a new aircraft. Such theoretical considerations of aircraft design must be seen against the background of the general fraternity (and sorority) of pilots. By the very nature of their selection processes and training, pilots were, and still are, expected to cope with any difficulties. For 99.999 per cent of the time the human pilot does cope, but now and then, when under stress, a badly positioned or poorly designed instrument can contribute to a disaster.

training and cockpit drill. In extreme cases, this lack has led to avoidable and sometimes fatal accidents.'

Under the pressure of war many minor hazards and irritations caused by equipment or its location in the cockpit could not be investigated or corrected without interrupting production. The wartime test pilots held their jobs because they were above-average pilots; they learnt to cope with many difficulties and, working under extreme pressure, they had little

CHAPTER SEVEN

MORE FIGHTING COCKPITS

An awkward example

Many aircraft introduced in the 1930s were designed for use in an air war as understood at the time. One year into the war that eventually came, deficiencies both in equipment and tactics were cruelly highlighted. The Bristol Blenheim is selected as an example of 1930s ideas on both air warfare and cockpit design having to remain in use in the 1940s.

The Blenheim I, like its civil precursor, had a continuous profile line for the nose and windscreen, with the pilot and observer (navigator) sharing the same set of transparencies. Subsequent versions were given an extended nose for the navigator's position and a conventional 'step' windscreen for the pilot, thereby bringing his eyes closer to the glass.

The Blenheim was designed to be flown left-hand-on throttles and right-hand on wheel, with most but not all of the engine controls arranged to the left hand. However, to ensure that the pilot's right hand also had plenty to do, the hydraulic selector controls for undercarriage, flaps and turret were alongside his right thigh. These were three identical push-pull handles, in line, and each working in the same sense. The designers had obviously recognized that they might be confused, so each one had its function engraved on the top. However, they did not consider what it was like to be a pilot encumbered in a flying suit in a dimly lit cockpit and reaching for one of the selectors. It was just too easy to select the wrong one and then, typically, having supposedly selected undercarriage down, nothing would happen because the hydraulic system, of limited power, was still feeding the gun turret.

Later marks were fitted with a very awkward catch on the undercarriage selector to distinguish it from the other two adjacent controls. In its declining years the Blenheim even sported a proper undercarriage selector lever. The propeller pitch push-pull knobs were below and behind the pilot's left elbow, with the two identical knobs of the carburettor cut-outs just below them. Again the designers had failed to consider the pilot's tasks. Admittedly the cut-outs were painted red but they had failed to realize that pilots did not usually have colour-sensitive eyes in their elbows. Should an engine fail on take-off then it was vital that the pilot selected coarse pitch on the failed engine and not the cut-out for the good engine.

Among the critical comments of a number of ex-Blenheim pilots are those of Air Vice-Marshal A. G. Dudgeon, which include the suggestion that a Blenheim pilot had to behave like a one-armed paperhanger and had to have a prehensile

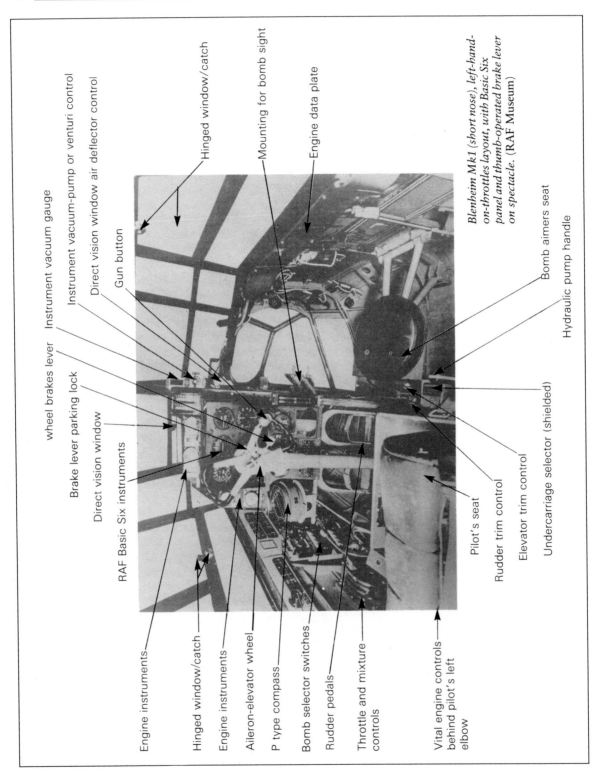

Instrument vacuum gauge

Instrument vacuum-pump or venturi control

Direct vision window air deflector control

Hinged window/catch

Mounting for bomb sight

Engine data plate

Gun button

wheel brakes lever

Brake lever parking lock

Direct vision window

RAF Basic Six instruments

Engine instruments

Hinged window/catch

Engine instruments

Aileron-elevator wheel

P type compass

Bomb selector switches

Rudder pedals

Throttle and mixture controls

Vital engine controls behind pilot's left elbow

Pilot's seat

Rudder trim control

Elevator trim control

Undercarriage selector (shielded)

Hydraulic pump handle

Bomb aimers seat

Blenheim Mk1 (short nose), left-hand-on-throttles layout, with Basic Six panel and thumb-operated brake lever on spectacle. (RAF Museum)

Civil and military aircraft cockpits today

Above *Airbus A 320.* (Airbus Industrie)

Right *Airbus A 320: night approach.*
(Rediffusion Simulation)

Above *Slingsby T67 Firefly trainer, with push-pull throttle knob, extensive radio equipment for training pilots to manage airways and control zone procedures, and a Basic T flight panel.*

Right *The Control and Display Unit of a Flight Management System (FMS).* (Smiths Industries)

Far right *Airbus A310: two-pilot flight deck with large overhead selector and indicator panel, and electronic displays for the primary flight instruments.* (Airbus Industrie)

Right *Modern electro-mechanical, plus some electronic, attitude director and horizontal situation displays.* (Sperry)

Below *Solid-state electronic engine instrument panel: the numerals are formed by arrays of light emitting diodes (LEDs).* (Smiths Industries)

Below right *Solid-state (LEDs) engine and systems panel for an airliner.* (Smiths Industries)

Far right *Night approach to a landing in a Boeing 747-400.* (Rediffusion Simulation)

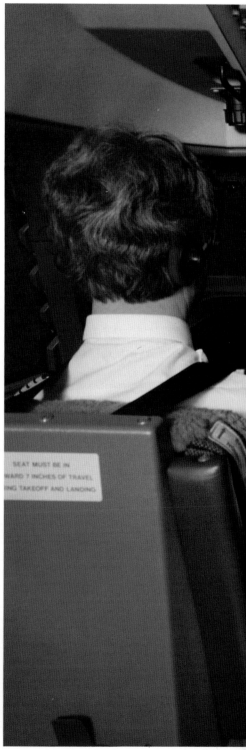

Left *Towards the 'glass cockpit' — the flight deck of the Boeing 747-400 with large, eight-inch square, colour CRT displays replacing all but a few of the conventional electro-mechanical instruments.* (Boeing)

Overleaf main picture *The MD 80 airliner. This much enlarged version of the ubiquitous DC 9 has a flight deck which incorporates many improvements in the overall ergonomics since the original model entered service in 1966.* (McDonnell Douglas)

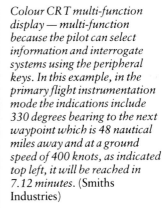

Colour CRT multi-function display — multi-function because the pilot can select information and interrogate systems using the peripheral keys. In this example, in the primary flight instrumentation mode the indications include 330 degrees bearing to the next waypoint which is 48 nautical miles away and at a ground speed of 400 knots, as indicated top left, it will be reached in 7.12 minutes. (Smiths Industries)

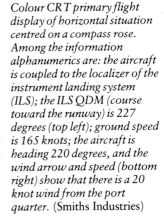

Colour CRT primary flight display of horizontal situation centred on a compass rose. Among the information alphanumerics are: the aircraft is coupled to the localizer of the instrument landing system (ILS); the ILS QDM (course toward the runway) is 227 degrees (top left); ground speed is 165 knots; the aircraft is heading 220 degrees, and the wind arrow and speed (bottom right) show that there is a 20 knot wind from the port quarter. (Smiths Industries)

Electronic flight instrument system: map and weather display. The aircraft's heading is 230 degrees and is achieving a track over the ground of 217 degrees because of the 23 knot wind on the starboard bow (bottom left). The intensity of precipitation is indicated by the green, yellow and red areas, the last being the most intense and indicating the greatest potential turbulence. (Smiths Industries)

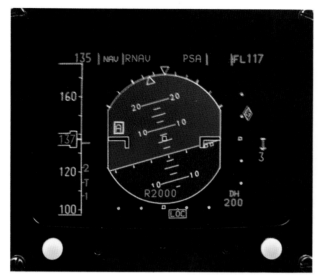

Above *Electronic flight instrument system (EFIS) in the primary flight mode displaying attitude, speed, vertical speed and altitude. The aircraft is in a 15 degree bank to the right and is at flight level 117 (11,700 feet); airspeed is 137 knots indicated; and vertical speed (the small arrow on the right) is minus 300 feet per minute.* (Smiths Industries)

Right *The Boeing 737. A feature of many Boeing airliners is the positioning of the undercarriage selector lever on the main instrument panel. This is a later version of the B 737 equipped with two flight management systems, the control and display panels of which can be seen in front of the two white thrust levers. The automatic flight control system panel is set into the coaming above the main panel. The individual selector knobs and switches enable the crew to 'dial' in the required speed, altitude, heading, airspeed and vertical speed. In addition, the flight control system can be commanded by the flight management systems.* (Boeing)

Middle left *The Boeing 737-400 was given an electronic instrument system similar to that of the 747 and 757/767. In addition, it has solid-state (LED) engine and systems instruments. The left-hand panel shows (left and right engines, reading from the top): low pressure shaft speed in per cent (N1); exhaust gas temperature (EGT); high pressure shaft speed (N2); fuel flow. The right-hand panel (top to bottom) shows: engine oil pressure; engine temperature; oil quantity, percentage remaining; vibration on a comparative scale of 0–5; hydraulic pressure and quantity remaining in systems A and B.*

Above left *The Boeing 757/767 flight deck, common to both aircraft types. Boeing's design philosophy includes 'a quiet, uncluttered layout', and is an example of one of the steps toward replacing all electro-mechanical instruments by electronic displays. The two-colour CRT displays on the centre of the panel provide engine data (upper) and systems information (lower).*

Left *Basic T layout of the primary flight instruments in an HS 125 jet. At one time the number and type of instruments fitted to a business/commuter aircraft were usually different from those to be found in the large airliners. But with increased speed, operating height and range, aircraft such as the HS 125 have to be equipped to the same standard as the big jets, as this photograph emphasizes. (British Aerospace)*

Right *In the 1980s threat and collision avoidance systems (TCAS) were introduced in the USA to reduce the number of 'airmisses' in congested airspaces. In place of a separate TCAS display, the 'threat' information is combined in this instrument with vertical speed indication (VSI). In this example the outer circle is the VSI with a large white triangular 'bug' to indicate fpm; the aircraft is climbing at about 1,000 fpm. 'Own' aircraft is at the centre of the circle of white dots representing a diameter of 4 nautical miles (nm). The blue diamond indicates another aircraft 1,100 feet lower and about 4 nm away at 11 o'clock. The yellow circle at 10 o'clock is an aircraft about 3 nm off and descending at more than 500 fpm. The red square is another 'target': this is at 1 o'clock about 3 nm off, 400 feet higher and climbing at more than 500 fpm. (Smiths Industries)*

Middle right *An example of an electro-mechanical instrument whose display information has been extended by the addition of a circle of LEDs. This is a VSI with an advisory TCAS indication (the red LED semicircle), which advises that the rate of descent should be 1,500 fpm or more to avoid a collision with another aircraft. (Smiths Industries)*

Left *One of the more simplified examples of HUD symbology. The aircraft heading is passing through 130 degrees, as indicated on the compass scale at the bottom of the display, in a left turn at 180 knots and at 1,800 feet. The dot and two bars form a perspective path in the sky pointing to the correct heading.* (Smiths Industries)

Bottom left *Head-up display in the air-to-air gun mode. The aircraft is flying at Mach 0.56 at 12,350 feet in a descending turn to the right. If the guns were fired at that moment the shell traces would appear to describe the curving path indicated by the dots. The circle of radiating lines is the aiming circle which the pilot has placed over the target, and is offset down to the left on the display by the computer. This takes into account the ballistic equations and the movement of the two aircraft. It is making the attacking aircraft pilot 'lead' the target to allow for the relative movements so that the shells and the target arrive at the same spot in space.* (Smiths Industries)

Right *This Harrier GR 3 cockpit is included to emphasize the extent to which colour has recently been added to the cockpit to improve the control interface. In this 1960s design cockpit, there is very little.* (British Aerospace)

Right *The cockpit of the Harrier II AV-8B/GR V of the USMC and the RAF. This later version of the Harrier STOVL fighter has an improved cockpit, the design of which incorporates interface technologies not available when the Harrier first appeared in the 1960s.* (McDonnell Douglas)

Far right *Hawk fighter/attack aircraft developed from the trainer version. Additional communications panels, HUD and weapon controls distinguish this from the trainer version.* (British Aerospace)

This illustrates the realism achieved with modern flight simulators. Of course only in a simulator would the pilot open the canopy when in flight! (McDonnell Douglas)

A General Dynamics F 16 cockpit, illustrating the effectiveness of modern cockpit lighting and the clarity of the electronic displays. The use of a side-stick control allows the central instrument panel to be extended downwards to make room for instruments otherwise displaced by the electronic displays. (GEC Avionics)

The McDonnell Douglas F 18 Hornet cockpit with three electronic multi-function display units on which the majority of the information needed by the pilot is presented. The left-hand CRT display is being used to present weapon status in a graphic format while the right-hand display is showing primary flight attitude information. On the left can be seen the two large thrust levers for the two engines. (McDonnell Douglas)

An illustration of a fighter cockpit in which the pilot is presented with three 'attack' mode views. Directly ahead the real world is combined with a TV image to overcome poor visibility conditions and with primary flight alphanumerics and symbols. The right-hand CRT is a FLIR (forward looking infra-red) view below the nose of the aircraft. The screen on the left is a map presentation. (GEC Avionics)

The cockpit of the EAP, the 1990s European Fighter demonstrator. The ergonomics take advantage of multi-function electronic displays, HOTAS and a sophisticated HUD and weapon-aiming system. Interestingly, in view of the trend in the late 1980s toward side-stick control, the EAP has the stick in the conventional position. (British Aerospace)

tail to back up his two hands as they groped among the identically shaped and awkwardly located controls. Such strong comments might have been even stronger had the Blenheim retained the engine nacelle mounted instruments of the earliest versions.

The Beaufort torpedo bomber from the same design office as the Blenheim had a similar well-fenestrated cockpit — one which offered little obstruction to the pilot's view of the flak streaming up from the target.

The central control pedestal included the rudder trim crank and indicator. The trim indicator perversely moved in the opposite direction to that of the crank. As with so many twin engined aircraft of that era, when an engine failed, directional control could not be maintained without reducing power on the good engine and winding on full rudder trim. Hence the need for a clear unambiguous rudder trim crank and indicator relationship; alas not in the Beaufort.

Although the central pedestal was designed as a logical, concentrated arrangement of the engine controls, the cowling gills were operated by a wheel to the pilot's left while the fuel cocks and engine cut-outs were below the pilot's right elbow.

Another British aircraft was the Botha. It had only a short life in the RAF but its cockpit design reflected many of the practices of the late 1930s. As a place in which to sit and see ahead, to each side and upward, it was better than many contemporary aircraft types. The right-hand windows were deeper than those on the left so that the pilot could keep a target in view on his starboard bow. The cockpit instruments, switches, levers and wheels were typical of the era. However, their location appears to have been dictated by mechanical convenience rather than by anticipation of any problems a pilot might have to meet in an emergency.

With its full operational load of fuel, torpedo and guns, the Botha had only a marginal single-engine performance.

Sudden engine failure during take-off needed the utmost pilot skill and experience to keep the aircraft flying. With the right hand adjusting the engine controls and the left on the control wheel, there was no free hand to turn the rudder trim; only having feathered the failed engine, and with the right hand moved to the wheel, was the left hand free to do so. Because the rudder trim worked in the wrong sense, the pilot's left and right juggling act was made even more complex. As with most aircraft, the undercarriage had to be raised as quickly as possible, and this meant feeling for a lever which moved in a five-position 'gearbox' gate. This selector lever for undercarriage and flaps had a catch, which added to the time taken to select 'gear up'. As might be

The Bristol Bombay, circa 1939. Note the elegant brass domed ignition switches. The thumb-operated brake lever is on the left of the wheel, as this is a right-hand-on-throttles layout. The cockpit was designed in the 1930s before the advent of the RAF Basic Six panel. Boost gauges and rpm indicators are kept apart, the former in front of the pilot, the latter over the door leading to the nose. (via Aeroplane Monthly)

expected, considering the era in which the Botha was designed, the fuel control panel was not in the cockpit. In most RAF aircraft the fuel controls and indicator panel might be seen and reached, even if this needed some contortion of the pilot's body, but in the Botha, like the Wellington, the fuel tank cocks were out of sight and out of reach, even if not out of mind.

In 1941 the cockpit of the Mosquito, the first twin-engined aggressive monoplane from de Havilland, was unique among RAF cockpits. Among a number of interesting features, compared with some of its contemporaries, the cockpit had all the essential knobs, switches and levers located forward of the pilot; there were no cunningly positioned hydraulic or fuel cocks necessitating a double-jointed arm-reach backwards and downwards to operate them. For the standards of its time the Mosquito cockpit was reasonably laid out. It was a

left-hand-on-throttles arrangement but with rudder and aileron trim controls, and flap and undercarriage levers, arranged for the pilot's right hand. In the fighter versions the control column was cranked to the right; in other versions there was a spectacle wheel for aileron control. The brakes were operated by the traditional British finger-grip lever on the control column or wheel.

As with most aircraft types, there was considerable variation in cockpit equipment among the different marks. Those versions in which the navigator was provided with attack radar had the right-hand side of the cockpit crowded with electronics and CRT displays.

The cockpit canopy, with its unsubstantial-looking frame, afforded the crew a virtually unobstructed view in most directions.

As with many RAF cockpits, space in some directions was at a premium. In the Mosquito the two crew members sat

Mosquito night fighter with airborne interception (AI) radar taking up much of the starboard side of the cockpit. The bomber version had a spectacle type aileron/elevator control. (Crown Copyright)

nearly shoulder to shoulder. Getting in and out when encumbered with flying clothing and equipment via the small door on the starboard side was not easy. Pilots were advised to stop the starboard engine and feather the propeller before baling out. A placard on the door carried the exhortation 'Beware of Airscrew.'

Every pilot learns to adapt to the idiosyncracies and shortcomings of cockpits, and such adaptation tends to disguise poor cockpit design. For example, how many Mosquito pilots were aware that their slightly skewed seating posture might induce a false sensation of turning when they were flying on instruments at night or in cloud? In the Mosquito the rudder pedals were offset inboard from the seat centre-line, because of the converging lines of the aircraft's nose.

When single-pilot aircraft, such as Mosquitoes and Beaufighters, were first used for long-range operations in the RAF, pilots were advised to keep as still as possible in their seats and let their posteriors become numb. Any attempt to ease one's seat could result in greater discomfort as the blood tried to recirculate.

The Mosquito offset seat effect was only one of a number of physical sensations and visual perceptual factors which took time to research. In the meantime aircrew continued to be killed. Without other evidence the majority of these accidents were attributed to 'pilot error'.

An example is that of the significantly numerous night take-off accidents to Wellington bombers in the mid-1940s. Aircraft would dive into the ground about three minutes after take-off. Not until 1949 was Professor A.R. Collar's report available. He pointed out that, in daylight, a pilot assessed the angle of climb after take-off from the pressure of the seat on his back and his view of the ground. At night, however, when deprived of attitude information from a view of the ground, a pilot was not able to distinguish the difference between a steady climb and acceleration using seat pressure alone.

At the top of the climb after take-off, when the pilot levelled the aircraft out, there was an increase in speed. This would give a sensation of pressure on the pilot's back. This was then interpreted as a climb effect. Therefore the pilot would push the aircraft's nose down to achieve, as he thought, level flight. In a vicious circle of cause and effect, the aircraft would be 'pushed over' into a fatal dive into the ground.

Had the pilots been given more positive instructions on the vital need to concentrate on their instruments and not to rely on physical sensations, then many such accidents might have been avoided. Of course, another contributory cause of these Wellington accidents was the wartime 'blackout', which required pilots to maintain attitude whilst flying in the 'black bowl' of night.

Contributory too was the use of constant-speed propellers. These kept engine revolutions and therefore engine sound at a constant level irrespective of the aircraft's speed, thus depriving the pilot of another indication that something was wrong.

British heavy bombers which came into service in the mid-war period played their part in the history of the pilot's place. The Lancaster for example. This was designed for a single-pilot crew, there being only one set of controls. This was in contrast to the American practice of usually having two pilots in the crew of large aircraft types.

The pilot had good arcs of view in all directions, with only a slight obstruction from the forward turret when taxying. The cockpit, with its canopy extended aft to include other crew members, kept the pilot, flight engineer, navigator and wireless operator close together and in some ways was similar to contemporary German practice, e.g. Junkers Ju88 and Dornier Do217.

The fuselage was as narrow as would permit carriage of the required bombload

Above *Avro York, circa 1945. The large flight deck transparencies were possible with an unpressurized fuselage, and pendant throttles were mounted as in many flying boats of the era.* (British Airways)

Above right *The air gunner/radar operator's position in an RAF DB7, circa 1941. By raising and turning the seat to face forward, the emergency primary and engine controls could be used; the latter can just be seen forward on the left.* (Crown Copyright)

and therefore there was only a slim gangway to starboard alongside the crew positions. However, in practice, and as with other RAF aircraft, the human clearance dimensions for fuselage cross sections used by designers did not always appear to take full account of bulky flying gear which turned aircrew into Michelin Men festooned with leads, pipes, clips and straps.

By the time the Lancaster entered service, greater thought had been given to the positioning of instruments, controls and equipment in the cockpit. This was important, because in 1942 crewing policy for all large aircraft apart from flying boats and long-range transports was one pilot plus a pilot's mate; the latter usually the flight engineer. This crew arrangement is reflected in the layout of the Lancaster, whereby the right-hand side of the cockpit was given over to engine, fuel and ancillary systems controls. Unlike the

Wellington, the Lancaster had a central throttle pedestal — a position which made it accessible to the flight engineer and, incidentally, enabled a dual-control version for training to be easily adapted from the standard Lancaster by adding a second set of wheel and pedals, whereas in the Wellington Trainer there had to be an additional set of engine controls.

The flight deck of the York used by RAF Transport Command was a combination of civil and service practices. The spacious fuselage cross section, eight feet wide in the cabin and about six feet at the flight deck, was very different from that of the Lancaster, from which the York had inherited major components.

With a high wing layout Avro decided to run all control rods, wires and circuits between the flight deck and the engines against the deckhead of the fuselage. This resulted in an overhead control 'pedestal' with pendant control levers, as in

American flying-boats. The generous expanse of Perspex moulded panels ahead, to both sides and above, gave the pilots an 'expansive' view.

Some aircraft types of the Second World War had a set of emergency controls for use by another crew member isolated from the pilot (a feature of some two-seat biplanes of the inter-war years). Examples were the Maryland and Boston DB7. The Maryland had an emergency set of primary controls which could be swung into position for use by the navigator in the isolated nose position. In the Boston the emergency controls were located in the wireless operator's position aft. The enlarged version of the Maryland, the Baltimore, had the same isolated pilot's cockpit.

A contemporary pilot comment was, 'I had never had my controls so sensibly and neatly laid out before me. A feature of the Baltimore's cockpit was the row of nearly identical switches, each distinguished from the others only by its adjacent placard.' This prompted another pilot to comment, 'I might as well be priming my starboard motor as lowering my port landing light. However, this strange sameness in the appearance of the various instruments and ancillary controls does give the pilot credit for being something other than a ham-fisted halfwit who, unless every knob is shaped differently and painted a different colour, is liable to land with his bomb doors open and his flaps up.'

This was an interesting observation, which introduces the fundamental choice between arranging the controls like the keyboard of a piano or making each clearly distinguishable from the others and grouping them in a logical manner. The first design approach predicates a concert pianist technique on the part of the pilot; the second takes human fallibility into account.

The Martin Baker MBV, which first flew in May 1945, did not go into production. Yet it must be included because it incorporated many lessons from the shortcomings of other aircraft. As well as its airframe's advanced design, the cockpit, controls and instruments were much in advance of those in other aircraft.

Martin Baker paid particular attention to the type and the layout of controls and instruments, and it would be many years before other designers followed suit. For one thing, the cockpit had a proper floor. It also had the side instrument panels set at an angle to avoid parallax when reading the instruments. To afford a good view ahead when on the ground, the nose of the MBV descended from the windscreen in a smooth curve towards the spinner — a distinct improvement, in contrast to the poor view from the long-nosed fighters of 1940 when taxying.

A Martin Baker MBV cockpit of 1944. For its time it was a commendable attempt to improve both the layout and therefore the ergonomics of the cockpit as well as facilitating maintenance of the instruments. (Martin Baker)

Consolidated B24, circa 1942. The engine instruments are toward the starboard side, while above the central controls pedestal can be seen the Honeywell autopilot control panel. The large black box with the 'radio' control knob alongside the four white throttle levers is the manifold pressure selector for the four exhaust gas turbine superchargers: the aileron/elevator wheels extend out of the instrument panel. (via Aeroplane Monthly)

Big Americans

One reason for the difference between American and British cockpits of the 1940s was the extent to which American aircraft were equipped with electrically operated and selected systems, whereas the majority of British aircraft still used mechanical 'pilot-powered' devices. Hence the greater number of wheels, crank handles and levers in the cockpit of a British-designed aircraft. There was a similar difference between British and German designs.

By 1942, more and more American aircraft were coming into the hands of pilots of other nationalities. One important example, the design of whose flight deck was in advance of many others, was the Consolidated B24 Liberator. The B24 introduced many pilots of the Second World War to an entirely different concept in controls, instruments and gadgets. Among the significant items were: lined, sound-insulated crew compartments; ashtrays; and well-padded, very adjustable seats for the two pilots. Unlike the British 'heavies', the B24 had two completely equipped side-by-side pilot positions with the captain on the left and the second pilot concentrating on what we could now term thrust and system management, using the comprehensive array of engine instruments on the forward panel.

Another interesting difference from British practice was the engine controls in the B24D (RAF Liberator III). The Pratt & Whitney Twin Wasps (S4C4–G) had exhaust-gas, turbine-driven superchargers with an early form of electronic automatic boost control. In addition there were the typical American switch-type propeller controls.

In some B24s, the dorsal gun turret was immediately abaft the flight deck. If the twin 0.5s were fired ahead, the vibration could dislodge all loose items such as lamp holders; the flight deck would fill with acrid fumes of burnt cordite.

As with all long-range aircraft, the crew of a B24 had to keep a close watch on fuel consumption. In the earlier versions of the B24 the tank contents could be checked using the readings on plastic 'boiler house' gauge glasses mounted on the aft bulkhead of the flight deck. These were connected directly and dangerously to the fuel tanks.

The B24 represented the best of early-1940s American aviation technology and its cockpit equipment reflected the advances which had been made since the B17 Flying Fortress was first introduced. The design of the controls and instruments of the B17 was similar to that of other Boeing four-engine aircraft: the B314 flying boat for example.

To avoid the 'obstacle course' between the door on the starboard side, near the tail, and the flight deck, the pilots, navigator, bomb-aimer and radio operator preferred the acrobatic use of the escape hatch beneath the cockpit. To get forward from the side door meant passing through the mounting for the ventral ball turret and then traversing the narrow catwalk between the bomb racks — a task made more difficult when wearing flying clothing and equipment.

Being an earlier aircraft, the cockpit of the B17 had fewer electrical systems switches and controls compared with the B24. There were throttle, propeller and mixture control levers for each engine along with a master control unit for all four exhaust turbine superchargers. The instrument panel arrangement was typical of the 1930s, with the majority of the flight instruments grouped on the central panel and with the engine instruments in front of the co-pilot. As

there was no separate engineer's panel the co-pilot managed the engines. A particular Boeing 'trade mark' was the design of the throttle levers, which could be operated as individual levers or in groups of two depending on which of the traverse bars were selected.

The around 30,000-feet cruising altitude of the B17 and an outside air temperature of minus 45 degrees Celsius (more than twice as cold as a domestic freezer) gave a far from comfortable ride for the crew. However, of all the crew positions, that of the two pilots was the least cold as well as being subjected to the least noise. Contributing to the comfort of the pilots were the small area of win-

The typical Boeing 'bar' type throttle levers for the four engines of this Boeing B17 enabled the pilot to move all four together, in pairs or individually. The autopilot control panel is at the back of the central controls pedestal. (via Aeroplane Monthly)

Lockheed P 38, circa 1942. Although a fighter aircraft, a wheel was provided and not a 'stick': The large black knob with the arrow outlined in white was the arming selector for the guns, and an oxygen supply regulator was mounted between the pilot's feet. (via Aeroplane Monthly)

dows and the use of very thick glass. As with most American aircraft, extensive use was made of an insulating lining for the crew positions.

The 'standard', side-by-side, two-pilot cockpit of so many American multi-engine aircraft of the Second World War was not applied to the Douglas Invader (A–26/B–26). This twin-engine attack/bomber, introduced into the USAAF in 1943, reverted to the single-place cockpits of medium bombers such as the Maryland and Boston. However, an important difference, and one which may have been influenced by British and German designs, was the provision of a gangway to the right of the offset pilot's position. This arrangement provided access to the navigator/bomb-aimer station in the extreme nose.

Unlike the Blenheim cockpit, which it resembled in layout, the Invader had a far better arrangement of controls and instruments. Again unlike the Blenheim, the throttle pedestal was on the centre line. A good point, and one which was so often lacking in contemporary British cockpits, were the 'close-to-hand' fuel cock selector levers. As in other American aircraft of the era, the fuel cocks were of good size, clearly marked and moving in a logical direction.

By the time the Invader was on the drawing board the production of multi-curved, large one-piece Perspex mouldings had advanced considerably since the 1930s. The Invader pilot was afforded a virtually uninterrupted view to both sides and upward and with only one centre windscreen pillar.

Although the Blenheim has been used for comparison, this is unfair chronologically because the Invader's designers had the benefit of technologies nearly ten years in advance of those available to Bristol Aircraft.

The Boeing B29 is another bomber whose cockpit design contributed a number of new ideas to the subject in general. This was the first large pressur-

The spacious flight deck of a Boeing B29, circa 1944. Each pilot had a control pedestal with throttle levers at his outboard side, and the two levers on the central pedestal are part of the brake control system. The fairing of the flight deck windows into the lines of the nose was the result of a move towards pressurized crew compartments. This provided a shape better able to resist the pressure loads at high altitude. (Boeing)

The Commander of a B 29. The majority of the engine instruments were allocated to the engineer's panel. The pilot has his hand on the emergency brake control handles, not on the throttles. (Boeing).

Right *A Junkers 188 in 1945. This improved version of the already successful Ju 88 had a non-stepped nose to the crew compartment. Pilot, air gunner, radar operator and others were positioned close together in the well-fenestrated nose.* (via Aeroplane Monthly)

Below *A study in noses. Left to right: B 17, B 29 and KC 97 tanker-transport at the end of the Second World War.* (via Aeroplane Monthly)

ized, high-altitude, long-range (5,000 miles) bomber.

The cockpit, or rather the flight deck, for it was flat-decked and spacious, was inside a continuously curved nose section and without a stepped windscreen. There were numerous separate sections of curved glass. Unfortunately when landing at night, particularly if it was raining, the pilot's view ahead of the runway lights was considerably impaired and distorted. Eventually some improvement was gained by using flat panels for those in front of the pilots.

The overall concept for the fenestration of the B29's nose derived from German designs, as did the groupings of the principal crew members together in one compartment.

Because of the width of the flight deck and the need for a gangway forward to the bomb aimer's station in the extreme nose, there was no central control pedestal as in the B17 and B24 for example. Each of the two pilots had a control ped-

estal at his outboard hand. The throttles on these pedestals for the four engines were the typical Boeing 'bar' type as used in the B17.

When it came to the B47 jet bomber Boeing departed from the traditional flight deck layout for bombers. In place of the standard side-by-side, two-pilot arrangement, the B47 had tandem cockpits under one transparent canopy similar to that of a fighter aircraft. Another interesting departure from tradition for pilot and gangway layouts was the positioning of the gangway to the left of the seats rather than to the right. A similar gangway position was adopted for the B45 Tornado of the USAF; the first of which flew in the same year, 1947, as the B47. With the B52 Boeing reverted to the traditional, side-by-side, flight deck. A distinguishing feature of the central control pedestal were the eight throttles: the pilots of the earlier Convair B36 had to get their hands around ten throttles.

Boeing B47 jet bomber, circa 1948, with a fighter-type canopy for the two pilots. (via Aeroplane Monthly)

Silent power

The cockpits of gliders have usually borrowed equipment and instruments from powered aircraft. Without attempting here a detailed study of the cockpits used for this type of flying, one military glider deserves specific mention. This is the Airspeed Horsa which took part in the 1944 Allied invasion of Europe.

The 'flight deck' of the Horsa had a number of good features which would, had certain considerations not dictated otherwise, have provided the ideal pilots' position. There were, for example, wide arcs of view up, around and down, and plenty of room.

The Horsa's aileron control wheels were of Handley Page HP42 size and the various levers were large and sturdy. The two pilots of the Glider Pilot Regiment shared one set of flight instruments — an economy which reflected the expendable nature of the glider's role.

Both tug and glider pilot had a distinctive tow release lever ready to hand as neither wanted a heavy cable hanging down. Indicative of the special nature of the glider pilot's task was the large airbrake lever set at his right hand, with another at the co-pilot's left hand. The Horsa had 'muscle powered' air brakes. In contrast the flaps and wheel brakes were actuated by compressed air.

Prone and supine

In their idle moments, if they had any, designers were wont to sketch unusual cockpit arrangements. Attempts were made to find an alternative to the upright seated position: for example the prone-pilot layout. Most were found to be impracticable. Just as man learned thousands of years ago that he could control a horse most effectively by sitting rather than lying on its back, so the pilot has for the past 85 years preferred to sit at the controls. Of course Santos Dumont did it standing up, as did the crew of most airships. Concessions have had to be made in recent years to mitigate the

The North American B45 Tornado, a contemporary of the B 47, had at least 40 engine instruments arranged in front of the pilot. The engine controls were to his right and the access gangway to the other crew positions was on the left. (via Aeroplane Monthly)

adverse effects of high G, and today the sitting position of the combat jet aircraft pilot is a compromise between reclining and the need for a clear path for body and seat when ejecting. In the middle of the Second World War the Focke Wulf 190's semi-reclining position was not adopted by the RAF or the USAAF because it limited the pilot's freedom to move his head around. The Supermarine solution, for the Spitfire, were the two-position rudder pedals. These enabled the pilot to fly with his feet in the upper position whenever it was necessary to indulge in high-G manoeuvres.

A prone pilot's position tried out in a Meteor jet fighter in the 1950s, to improve the pilot's tolerance to high G forces, was not successful. Two reasons for abandoning the idea were the difficulties in installing a 'prone' ejection seat and the 'neckache' posture for the pilot. Another unusual cockpit was that of the Leduc 0–21 of 1955 contained within the sharply pointed nose cone of the intake

duct to the jet engine. This 'intake' cockpit was pressurized and in an emergency could be separated from the fuselage — after which its descent was controlled by a parachute.

Its design was anticipated by the Miles M52 supersonic project. The M52 was designed in 1943 and would have incorporated a number of very advanced features for its time, including a cockpit housed in the nose intake cone. Consideration had to be given to a number of things which in 1943 meant entering uncharted waters. For one thing, what if the pilot had to abandon the aircraft at speeds above Mach 1.5? At that time in the UK and in the middle of an all-out war, the ejection seat was not available. Thus it was decided that the complete cockpit section would be separated by explosive charges from the intake section. A parachute in the 'tail' of the cockpit would be automatically deployed once clear of the M52 to slow the descent and give time for the pilot to bail out using his

Prone pilot Meteor of 1952. (via Aeroplane Monthly)

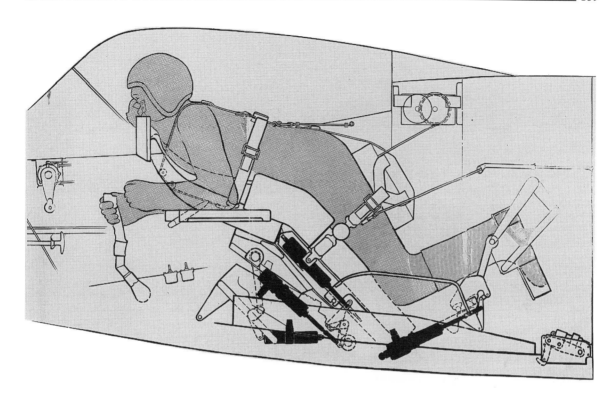

normal parachute.

A Grumman F7F Tigercat, twin-engine fighter, was used to evaluate a variable position pilot's seat. The seat could be in the normal position for take-off and landing, in the three-quarter back position for combat and in the fully supine position for long-range cruising flight. Captain Eric Brown, RN, described how he tried the seat in the three different positions. He found the supine position rather alarming, particularly in the vertical part of a loop. He advocated the prone position rather than the supine.

The rapid advances made in aircraft speeds and operating altitudes as well as operational effectiveness between 1939 and 1945 were not matched by instrument development. Few new cockpit instruments appeared during the war years. The instrument companies had to produce instruments to standard designs which did not necessarily reflect the state of the technology. Many instrument types had to be retained far longer than

technical experience should have indicated. The policy of the Air Ministry in Britain during the Second World War was firstly to have maximum interchangeability of instruments among the many different types of aircraft and, secondly, once a particular instrument had proved to be acceptable for a number of different aircraft types then only a serious defect or operational shortcoming would justify a change. Therefore non-critical modifications were avoided because they might affect interchangeability, spares and the training of service personnel.

Although versions of the airspeed indicator were always available calibrated in knots, the greater demand in the 1920s and 30s was for indicators calibrated in statute miles per hour. Those who used charts for navigation, such as flying boat and long-range aircraft crews, usually worked in nautical miles and knots because of the direct relationship between a minute of latitude and the nautical mile.

Prone pilot Meteor. The catch mechanism bottom right released the seat and pilot downward in the event of having to abandon the aircraft. This illustration bears some comparison with that of da Vinci's flying machine (see page 13)! (via Aeroplane Monthly)

Right *The Leduc 0–21 ram jet of the 1950s, with the pilot seated in the nose cone of the air intake to the engine.* (via Aeroplane Monthly)

German, Italian and French aircraft had instruments calibrated in kilometres per hour to accord with their maps and charts.

In Britain during the Second World War a change was made to knots and nautical miles to bring all RAF commands into line with Coastal Command. At the end of the war civil aviation adopted the same standards for the simple reason that the majority of pilots and navigators were ex-RAF. With the gradual adoption of the ICAO Blue Table of international units for civil aviation and the change to the use of the nautical mile by the USAF and not just by the US Navy, the use of mph and statute miles became less common. Even the Space Shuttle works to distances in nautical miles.

The following table emphasizes that a mixture of units was chosen to avoid confusion in messages, particularly when using RT. This table is used by the majority of the world's aviation outside Russia.

ICAO Universal units of measurement

Long distances	Nautical miles
Short distances, i.e. runways, cloud height and visibility	Metres
Altitudes and heights	Feet
Horizontal speed	Knots
Vertical speed	Feet per minute
Visibility	Kilometres or metres
Wind speed and direction	Knots and degrees
Weight	Kilogrammes
Temperature	Degrees Celsius

NB. The standard nautical mile is 6,080 feet and is based on the average distance of one minute of latitude on the surface of the earth. Therefore if an aircraft's navigation system detects a change in aircraft position of, say, one degree (60 minutes) north or south then this gives a read-out of 60 nautical miles. The knot is one nautical mile per hour.

At one time the presence of a wheel for aileron control usually signified that you were in a big, slow-response aircraft. With the advent of bombers having powered controls, the big wheel needed to multiply the pilot's muscle power became unnecessary. The Vulcan, despite its massive size was controlled through fighter-type sticks in front of each pilot.

In many first-generation jet fighters, the cockpit was equipped with instruments whose details were little different from those of the piston-engine age. The early Vampire cockpit, for example, was hardly distinguishable from that of contemporary non-jet fighters. Only a few additional engine instruments, such as a jet-pipe temperature gauge and an rpm indicator reading well above the piston engine limit of around 3,000, gave the clue that the cockpit was in a jet fighter.

The earlier Meteor variants had an instrument panel which reflected the importance of jet pipe temperature and engine rpm. In piston-engined fighters the engine instruments were usually disposed to one side of the Basic Six panel. Meteors, such as the Mk.8, had a twin jet-pipe temperature indicator immediately below the gyro heading indicator. This was flanked by the two rpm indicators, and all needed to be within the pilot's normal instrument-scanning pattern.

The Meteor's throttle levers were unusual because they were just two small side-by-side knobs moving in fore and aft slots along the top of the port console.

Compared with even the high performance piston-engined aircraft such as the F8–F Bearcat, Tempest and Sea Fury, the new jets had thirsty engines. During a typical Meteor jet sortie the two engines used up to 400 gallons of fuel. As much as 40 gallons would be used for starting up, taxying and take-off. With a nominal

Far left This might be the instruments for a 1945 fighter, but closer inspection reveals a temperature indicator graduated up to 350 degrees Celsius and an rpm indicator extending up to 10,000. These are the instruments for a DH Vampire jet fighter which at first sight look little different from those of contemporary piston-engined aircraft.

tankage of 500 gallons the landing circuit at the end of a flight might be joined with only 60 gallons left in the tanks — just enough to go around for a second attempt if necessary. Therefore the fuel contents indicators were positioned close to the flight instruments.

Later versions of the Meteor, such as the NF11, had not only greater range but better radio navigational equipment. The familiar directional gyro at the bottom centre position on the standard panel was replaced by a radio compass, and they also had Machmeters, for around Mach 0.8 the Meteor gave the pilot some handling problems. The need to keep a watchful eye on fuel consumption, and on the Machmeter whenever the throttles were pushed to the stops, was offset by the far less complicated engine controls compared with those of a piston-engined air-craft; essentially just one lever for each engine.

The cockpit canopy of the Meteor family went through the usual evolutionary phases so familiar to other aircraft types of the 1940s. The Mk.Ia had a three-unit canopy: forward three-piece windscreen, hinged to starboard opening section and faired section blending into the fuselage. Access was on the 'traditional' left side. Later marks had a sliding canopy. With the tandem-seat trainer version the one-piece canopy was hinged along one side. The use of 12 separate panels showed the difficulty at that time of moulding one-piece canopies of large size. The Mk.8 had a canopy similar to that of the earlier single-seat aircraft, with the exception that the non-sliding rear part was metal and not Perspex.

CHAPTER EIGHT

THE PUPIL'S PLACE

Ab initio

In the first ten years of powered flying there were few aircraft types designed for instructing the ab-initio pilot. There were usually only the alternatives of: clinging alongside the pilot's seat and observing what had to be done to effect control; or, listening to the instructor in a classroom and watching from the ground as he demonstrated handling techniques; followed by 'Now off you go. Remember what I told you. And, try not to break the machine or your neck.'

The Wright Brothers evolved side-by-side, two-seat versions of their Flyer series as trainers.

In the first half of World War One a persistent cause of incidents and accidents involving pupils was the lack of a standard system of flying training. 'Sorry Sir, I've rather bent it. But Mr X told me to do it that way', the pupil would say. Smith Barry of the RFC quickly grasped the solution to the problems of training and introduced both *Pilot's Notes* for each type of aircraft and a standard curiculum of evolutions and instructor's 'patter' for the Central Flying School. By 1917 flying instruction in the RFC and the RNAS, at least, was standardized, to the benefit of the quality of training and to the reduction of accidents.

The history of training aircraft and their cockpits highlights a difference of opinion which applies to all the major 'aviation' nations: should the student pilot sit beside the instructor or be seated in tandem.

The ab initio training aircraft of many civil and air force flying schools have throughout the years tended to favour the tandem seating arrangement. For pupils who intended to become fighter pilots the tandem arrangement provided a degree of isolation. It also economized on the design and production of training aircraft by adapting existing types to provide room for an instructor's cockpit.

However, it is unsafe to generalize on tandem seat layouts when it comes to a question of who sits in front, the pupil or the instructor. In the RAF, for example, ab initio pilots in the 1930s and 40s sat behind the instructor in the Tiger Moth and the Magister. Among the reasons for this were: when the aircraft was flown solo there was no need to add compensating ballast weights because the instructor's seat was close to the aircraft's centre of lift; if the instructor's seat were aft of the pupil's seat, then when he got out the aircraft would have become excessively nose heavy, and vice versa when he got in. This applied particularly to small aircraft, which cannot tolerate fore and aft movements of heavy loads such as the pilots. As with the fore-and-aft sensitive

The Blackburn B2 'side-by-side' trainer. (British Aerospace)

Camel of the First World War, a pilot's weight was a significant part of the total weight of the aircraft. And if the pupil had to practice instrument flying 'under the hood', the extendable cover which enclosed the otherwise open cockpit would obstruct the view ahead if the instructor sat in the rear cockpit. In Britain the Blackburn B2 was, for its time, *c.*1939, an exception to the tandem arrangement because pupil and instructor were seated side by side.

Examples of opposites are the Bulldog Trainer, which had the instructor's cockpit aft, whereas the Hawker Hart Trainer had the hooded cockpit for the pupil behind the instructor.

The larger and more powerful trainers used at intermediate and advanced schools in the RAF in the 1940s, such as the Harvard and the Master, were arranged so that the pupil occupied the front seat.

With the instructor in front of his pupil, the instructor could observe, through the rear view mirror, the different expressions on the pupil's face: smile of relief at looping without falling off the top; intense concentration during a landing; 'sorry, I'm lost' expression during a navigational exercise. From the front cockpit the instructor could convey his commands and opinions with hand and arm signals, such as: both arms in the air, then down and hands clasping helmeted head, which was sometimes more effective than oaths shouted through the Gosport tube; left arm held out straight just before the flare to remind the pre-solo pupil that he must not look directly down at the ground when judging height.

One's first aircraft usually remains as a very clearly defined memory. The legendary 'old but not bold' pilots look back over 50 years with affection at, for example, the Tiger Moth. Many recall the cockpit, primitive even by late 1930s standards; the fact that there was very little room for a big flying boot in the space between the side of the instructor's seat and the fuselage side; and the pupil's forward view, much of which was occupied by the upper wing, struts, flying and landing wires and sometimes by an oversize instructor in the front seat. The Tiger Moth was not an easy aircraft to fly well; it required concentration on the part of the pilot for most of the time. As for executing a three-point landing without letting the Tiger leap into the air again, that was another special skill which had to be acquired and which was not made easier by the confused forward view. The late Ron Gillman, DFC, DFM, a gallant and most experienced flyer, when talking about his Tiger Moth days, mentioned that he found landing very difficult at first. Only after he stationed himself well to the side of the landing area and was able to observe the precise moment, angle and speed adopted by the more experienced pilots was he able to make a succession of good three-point landings. Talking of the cockpit in particular he remembered, as do many other Tiger Moth pilots and pilots of similar aircraft, the distraction of the blast of cold air and the noise when flying in an open cockpit.

To simplify the electrics on Tiger Moths there was only one pair of ignition switches. These were mounted outside, between the two cockpits. One advantage was that the 'prop swinger' could see, on the command 'switches off', that they were in the down position. Later versions of the Tiger Moth did not have this safety feature.

Compared with the Moth from which it was derived, the Tiger Moth's centre section was moved forward to give an easier exit for the instructor should he have to bale out. In consequence the wings had to be swept back to keep the

DH Tiger Moth two-seats-in-tandem trainer. Compared with the Moth, from which it was derived, the Tiger Moth's centre section was moved forward to facilitate bailing out of the front cockpit. (via Aeroplane Monthly)

The Tiger Moth aft cockpit. This is an export version and equipped with a machine gun and Aldis sight, but the cockpit details are typical of all Tiger Moths, apart from the cocking (arming) lever for the gun at the right side of the instrument panel and the absence of a Gosport speaking tube. Note the narrow spaces in which thick flying boots had to reach the rudder pedals. (British Aerospace)

centre of lift in the correct position. This is a rare example of an aerodynamic change to suit a cockpit design requirement.

Tiger Moth interlude

An oft-told story — one of many — about flying the Tiger Moth, either apocryphal or elaborated from frequent retelling, concerns an aged pupil pilot and a harassed instructor at a civilian flying school.

Beset with paperwork and a busy programme of flying, and by visibility which had varied throughout the day, the instructor tells the next pupil to go ahead and start up the aircraft. The aged pupil does so and is followed some minutes

later by the instructor, who leaps into the cockpit, uses the Gosport speaking tube and orders, 'Alright Mr Smith, taxi out and take off'. As the aircraft moves across to the take-off point the instructor busies himself with strapping in and with keeping a sharp lookout for other aircraft landing in the marginal conditions of rain and the failing evening light.

Mr Smith turns into wind, all is clear, and within a minute the Tiger Moth is airborne and quickly enters cloud. 'Good take-off. Now I have control. Er ... Well no. Carry on Mr Smith. Climb above cloud.' The hesitation at the words 'have control' came as the instructor's hand felt for the control column which was not there. For the previous flight the aircraft had been flown solo. The joystick had been removed and stowed in the locker behind the rear cockpit so that it could not be entangled by the seat harness.

The combination of the pupil's virtual inability to land except in good visibility, of having no means of controlling the aircraft himself, and the absence of parachutes in a civil trainer, warranted desperate measures. 'Mr Smith, level off now and maintain a heading of one eighty. And Mr Smith, please ignore anything I might do during the next few minutes. Concentrate on flying straight and level.'

Despite concentrating on flying straight and level and on course, the pupil could not but notice the strange antics of the instructor, who had undone his harness and was climbing over the side of the cockpit. For a moment Mr Smith imagined that he was about to witness a suicide which in the end would involve himself.

However, he felt slightly reassured when his instructor, who was carefully holding on to the sides of the two cockpits and feeling for a foothold, smiled with an expression intended to convey the impression that this apparent stunt was customary. The pupil could not see the instructor's hand open the locker and grab the stick. But he could not fail to see the haste with which he regained the front cockpit. 'Thank you, Mr Smith. I've got her.'

In the Miles Master, the RAF's first high-performance monoplane trainer, the pupil pilot sat in a fully equipped 'fighter' cockpit which resembled in complexity the pilot's place in the Hurricane or Spitfire to which he hoped to graduate. Compared with the two operational fighter cockpits, the Master had a much tidier arrangement of controls, with all the important items concentrated at the pilot's left hand. The instructor aft had a duplicate set of essential instruments and controls. On the first version of the Master to enter RAF service the canopy was in two sections, each hinged so that it lifted up to the right. However, this design proved to be too fragile for service use and was therefore changed to the more usual sliding type.

To give the instructor a reasonable view ahead when taking off or landing, a section of the canopy above his head would hinge upwards as the seat was raised to form a windscreen. Should the pupil pilot let the speed build up too much then the instructor's screen would fold down with unfortunate results; conversely it might spring open suddenly as the aircraft entered a spin.

From Tiger Moth or Magister to Harvard was one of the possible progressions for a trainee RAF Pilot in the 1940s. The Harvard cockpit, particularly its instruments and equipment, was different from British practice. The instrument layout reflected American instrument-flying techniques. It did not have, for example, the RAF Basic Six of airspeed, attitude, and vertical speed in the top row, and altimeter, gyro heading indicator, and turn and bank in the bottom row. These instruments, or their equivalents, were arranged in a seemingly less ordered manner. But this was nevertheless to what tens of thousands of American pilots became accustomed in all sizes and types of aircraft.

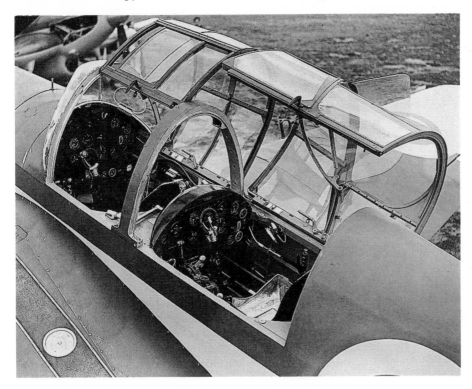

An early version of Miles Master trainer, circa 1939. The two canopies hinged up to the right, but this design proved unacceptable to the RAF and was replaced by sliding sections for the front seat pupil and the instructor. Note the two handles stowed on the decking behind the front seat — these were used for hand cranking the Kestrel engine. (via Aeroplane Monthly)

Instruments and controls in the front cockpit of a Miles Master, which was used to train pilots up to Hurricane and Spitfire standard. However, the Master's controls were arranged in a more logical manner than those of the two fighters; for example, the engine, propeller, flaps, undercarriage and landing lamp controls were concentrated at the pilot's left hand. The pipe coming out of the top of the instrument panel is the Gosport intercommunication tube from the instructor's cockpit. As with the majority of RAF trainers before and during the Second World War, the Master was not, at first, equipped with an 'intercom' or radio. (via Aeroplane Monthly)

Miles Control Unit in the instructor's cockpit of a Master. (via Aeroplane Monthly)

As with the Master, the engine controls of the Harvard were concentrated at the pilot's left hand. Again, as in the Master, the instructor's seat was behind the pupil's position. When flown solo the control column in the back cockpit could be removed to prevent it becoming entangled with the seat harness.

One big difference between the cockpits of these two trainers — and one which reflected national preferences — was the control column brake lever of the Master and the toe-operated brakes on the rudder pedals of the Harvard. Another difference was the hand-cranked, in-line, liquid-cooled, V12 RR Kestrel engine of the Master 1 and the typical American inertia starter of the Harvard's air-cooled radial. The latter was controlled by a rocking foot pedal: heel down to start the electric motor which 'spun up' the flywheel of the inertia starter; then toe down to start the engine.

The RAF's principal twin-engine trainer was the Oxford. This had a side-by-side, pupil on the left, cockpit. Some thought had been put into arranging the instruments and controls in a logical manner.

The majority of levers and switches for the more important functions were grouped on a central controls pedestal. These usually included a dummy propeller-pitch lever even though the Oxford had fixed pitch airscrews. The dummy lever enabled cockpit drills to be learnt correctly by pupil pilots in anticipation of the day they graduated to more advanced aircraft types.

As the Oxford was intended for the training of pilots for all multi-engine types, the left-hand instrument panel included the RAF Basic Six group of instruments. The instructor's panel did not have this standard panel and was equipped only with an airspeed indicator, altimeter and turn and bank indicator in addition to the engine instruments.

Earlier reference was made to 'contact' flying, particularly in the USA. During the Second World War, aircrews who trained in North America became accustomed to the 'chessboard' appearance of the terrain. The regular pattern of fields and roads along with clearly defined railway lines and rivers simplified navigation. Also, the more predictable weather was an advantage. In contrast, the visibility for much of the time in the United Kingdom, to which the new crews graduated, was poor. Their navigation and airmanship tasks included 'reading' the confused ground pattern of small fields, villages, narrow twisting lanes and streams and numerous railway lines. Adding to their problems was the standard RAF arrangement of station buildings and hangars. From the air one station looked like another, particularly in East Anglia. Hence special 'European familiarization' schools had to be established.

CHAPTER NINE

POST-WAR DEVELOPMENTS

Bombers into transports

During the Second World War civil aviation interests realized that air transport had developed considerably and that the future of world passenger transport was without doubt in the air.

The two major Western Allies, the UK and the USA, entered the post-war transport business with completely different ideas and equipment. The USA had immediate access to a vast number of military freight aircraft, such as the C54 Skymaster and the C47 Dakota, which could be converted quickly to passenger use. The DC4 (C54) was rapidly developed after the war, along with the Stratocruiser and the Constellation. But in the UK, despite starting to plan for post-war air transport in the course of the war, there was no successful passenger aircraft.

The Wellington was re-worked as the Viking and was given a two-pilot flight deck; the Lancaster and Halifax were developed into passenger and cargo transports but their cockpits were only slightly different from the bomber versions; albeit the York, derived from the Lancaster, was given a 'civil', two-pilot, flight deck at its inception.

Between 1945 and 1960, when the turbo-prop and the jet became the main means of air transport, there were few revolutionary changes to the flight deck.

In the first post-war decade of civil aviation in the USA, flight decks were little different from those of the air force transports from which many of the aircraft types had been derived. The DC4, four piston engines, was the progenitor of a long line of derivative types, each larger and more versatile than the one before. By the time the DC7C entered service in 1953 its four, turbo-compound, Wright R–3350 18-cylinder engines demanded extensive controls and instrumentation. The original flight deck dimensions of its ancestor, the C54, still applied, with the result that it was crowded with instruments and controls. A flight engineer was carried to look after the four engines and to monitor the total of 72 cylinders, 288 valves, 144 spark plugs plus the exhaust-driven turbo-superchargers. On transoceanic flights a navigator was also included in the crew because the aircraft was operated away from the airways and their radio navigational aids.

The Constellation, like its rival the DC7C, was developed progressively over the years to give increased speed and range. From the beginning it had a comprehensively equipped flight deck with an engineer's station. Incidentally, photographs of American four-engine transport aircraft of this period and also of military flight decks show the

The DC7C flight deck, circa 1955, with Basic T arrangement for the primary flight instruments, two sets of throttles, weather radar scopes, and twin-pointer engine instruments. The flap lever at the back of the controls pedestal is shaped like a flap; the undercarriage lever is shaped like a wheel. The rudder trim wheel is mounted above the instrument panel. (Smiths Industries)

Lockheed Constellation, circa 1950. The structural requirements for pressurization limited the size of the windows, which would not meet modern arcs of view requirements. The instruments are arranged pre-Basic T and pre-attitude director with both a zero reader and an artificial horizon in front of each pilot. (British Airways)

Boeing Stratocruiser, circa 1945. Access to the pilots' seats was from their outboard sides. The flight engineer could either face forward and adjust the engine settings, using the central pedestal controls or face to the right and monitor the systems panel. (Smiths Industries)

preference for twin-pointer engine instruments to save panel space. A typical centre panel would have two rpm indicators side by side. The left indicator would have two pointers, one carrying the figure 1 for the outboard left engine and the other the figure 2 for the inboard engine. The right-hand instrument would apply to engines numbers 3 and 4. The numbering of engines from left to right in the direction of flight became an established stereotype.

With the DC7C and the Constellation a pattern was definitely set for the layout of instruments and controls for multi-engine transports which was adopted world-wide: duplicate flight instrument panels with a centre engine instruments panel and a central pedestal for the throttles and other principal controls.

Of course, there were many variations in detail among the flight decks of the dif-ferent types of aircraft. For example, the Boeing Stratocruiser flight deck had access to the pilots' seats via their outboard sides. The flight engineer's desk and panel was on the starboard side behind the second pilot, with a gangway outboard leading to the pilot's seat. The flight engineer's seat could either be positioned so that he either faced to the right or, by swinging the seat round, faced forward between the two pilots. The central pedestal extended aft, with a second set of engine control levers for use by the flight engineer. A similar arrangement was adopted in a number of other transport aircraft types.

For some years controls and instruments in jet aircraft were little different from those used in piston-engine aircraft. The first passenger jets, such as the DH Comet, the Tupolov 104 and the Boeing 707, had flight decks arranged for two pilots plus other crew members such as navigators and flight engineers. The pressure to reduce all transport aircraft crew complements to just two pilots was some way off.

The pioneering de Havilland Comet DH 106 jet airliner, despite a set-back in its first year of service (1953) because of structural failures, went on to have a remarkably long life. The designers of its flight deck had few precedents to consult. They were very much on their own. Today this flight deck exhibits its 40 years and looks like an aviation antique. But for its time it represented an important set of design solutions.

One of the first details to be settled was the shape of the aircraft's nose and the flight deck window line — stepped, as with the majority of contemporary airliners, or a smooth pointed shape in which the nose and fenestration formed a smooth line, as specified for the Victor bomber then under development ten miles to the south of Hatfield at Handley Page, Cricklewood.

Apart from aesthetic considerations, the non-stepped nose imposed a structural penalty, for in order to provide an adequate vertical arc-of-view the windows had to be much larger than with a stepped nose.

In 1945, when the Comet was on the drawing board, not much was known either about how to make or use large areas of multi-layer, heated transparencies for windows. Also, at that time there were few pressurized passenger aircraft from which to gather in-flight experience of structural loads. The few military pressurized aircraft had limited window area, or, as in the B29, a multiplicity of small windows. Therefore de Havilland entered dangerous and uncharted waters when it chose a cabin differential pressure of 9 lb per sq. in. A small value until you relate it to a window over one foot square; then the total load is getting on for a ton. So not only had the windows to be tough, their framework had to be an

DH Comet, circa 1955. The flight deck crew positions are crowded together in the converging lines of the nose, the pilots seated close to the forward windows to maximize their arcs-of-view, with the systems engineer's panel on the right. (Smiths Industries)

Nose of a Handley Page Victor bomber, circa 1955. (via Aeroplane Monthly)

Caravelle, circa 1960. Although derived from the nose of the DH Comet, the Caravelle flight deck had a very different arrangement of the instruments and in general was more advanced. (Smiths Industries)

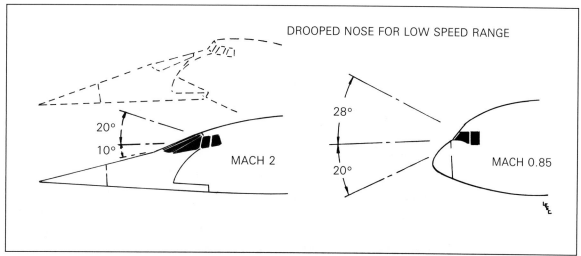

DROOPED NOSE FOR LOW SPEED RANGE

20°
10°
MACH 2

28°
20°
MACH 0.85

Mach 2 and Mach 0.85 noses, showing typical vertical up and down arcs of view. (Author)

extremely elaborate one-piece forging. Having settled the profile of the nose, the designers then faced the problems of spaces, volumes and arcs-of-view — problems which still have to be solved with modern cockpit and flight deck design.

A number of conflicting factors have to be resolved. A simple example is the pilot's eye position in relation to the forward windows. Ideally this needs to be close to the glass in order to maximize the arcs-of-view. But that would conflict with the required view of the instruments and with access to all the controls. The driver of a car has wide angles of view because the eyes are only about 30 inches from the windscreen.

Once pilot experience, in hours, accumulated, the flight deck of the Comet came in for some criticism — particularly concerning the need for 'musical chairs' when one member of the crew had to gain access to his seat.

A colour detail on the Comet's flight deck was the use of matt grey instrument panels at a time when the majority of aircraft had black panels.

Perhaps the decision to use the design of the nose section of the Comet, including much of the flight deck, for the Sud Aviation Caravelle, is an acknowledgement of the standard achieved by de Havilland.

The non-stepped windscreen nose went out of fashion in the early 1960s. The principal civil transport manufacturers since then have tended to adopt a stepped type nose with a V-shaped windscreen for the flight deck. Although not necessarily aerodynamically perfect, this profile affords the pilots the maximum arcs-of-view.

The advent of supersonic passenger aircraft, such as Concorde and its unsuccessful Russian copy, introduced the variable, drooping, nose. Up and sharply pointed for Mach 2; drooped to expose a more conventional forward flight deck windscreen.

To be mentioned is the rapid growth of electronic systems from the mid-1950s onwards for improving the safety and efficiency of flight, which included improving the information given to the pilot. One of the first practicable electronic displays was weather radar, which provided a clear indication of the best course to avoid centres of excessive turbulence and associated rapid up and down movements of the air mass. The Decca Navigator system deserves special mention because it gave the pilot an immediate and continuous visual display of aircraft position. A chart moved under a pen which marked both the position and the track of the aircraft. It contributed much to the efficiency of air transport in

Concorde. To operate this Mach 2 transport safely and economically requires an extensive array of instruments and controls on the systems panel, which takes up all the space on the right-hand side of the flight deck. (via Aeroplane Monthly)

Britain. Eventually inertial navigation systems came into use in the 1960s which had an important effect on both the design of the flight deck and operating methods as well as crew complements.

Despite the efforts of the researchers into human factors in aviation and of the pilots themselves in establishing safe and efficient standards for the flight deck, design offices still tended to go their own way. Yet it is easy to criticize with the benefit of hindsight, and aircraft designers in general must not be assigned all the blame. After the Second World War, for instance, it took some time for pilot opinion to gel and for standards to materialize. At the same time the airlines often failed to insist on standardization of flight decks among the different aircraft types in their fleets.

By about 1955, in Britain designers began to listen to the opinions and requests of the professional pilots association and not just to the test pilots and airline management pilots. Co-operation between test, management and the line pilots helped to evolve better flight decks. For example, pilots in general preferred that the coaming, or glare shield, above the instrument panel should be a horizontal straight line so as to provide a lateral reference during landing; and that the Basic T of airspeed, attitude, altitude and heading indicators be set close to the underside of the coaming to facilitate the transition from 'instrument' flight to 'visual' flight when executing an approach to land in marginal visibility conditions.

These are small points in themselves

and they and others helped to improve the overall ergonomic standard of the flight deck. Other details, which up to that time had not always been provided, were: holders for coffee cups and proper stowage for the pilots' flight bags, which in the days before computer-based performance and management systems had to include a number of large flight, performance and operating manuals. The provision of coffee cup holders was encouraged by the significant number of electrical failures among the world's transport aircraft caused by spilt coffee flowing down the openings in the central control pedestal.

The Sabre

Military cockpits during the late 1940s still retained much from the war years. This was a period of advancing the piston-engine types to the limit while at the same time converting air forces to jet power.

Among the more important fighters in the early 1950s was the F86 Sabre. Its cockpit was in many ways in advance of its contemporaries.

Without doubt the Sabre's designer had taken note of the fact that fighter pilots needed to be given a good all-round view if they were going to 'mix it with MiGs'. The pilot sat high in the fuselage within a large one-piece moulded plastic canopy. This canopy was hinged aft and was sometimes used as an airbrake once the wheels were firmly on the runway.

Pilots liked the provision made for easy access to the cockpit: steps and retractable handholds as well as the shelf formed by the open ammunition door.

The Sabre's instrument panel continued the American practice of arranging the instruments in an apparently random order. For example, the centre of the panel was taken up by a large heading indicator; the artificial horizon was to the right, with a fuel quantity gauge below; and the needle turn and bank indicator was alongside the vertical speed indicator in the bottom row. Dominating the main instrument panel in the D version of the F86 was the radar-ranging gyro gunsight. This meant that other important instruments had to be pushed to the sides of the panel.

Despite the arrangement of the cockpit, the F86 was, in general, liked by

The cockpit canopy of this North American F 86K Sabre is typical of the jet fighters of the 1950s and '60s and not very different from the piston-engined fighter canopies of the late 1940s. (via Aeroplane Monthly)

The McDonnell Douglas F4 Phantom which has performed so successfully for so many years with so many air forces that its cockpit must be included. The scope of the attack radar is mounted under the gun sight at the top of the main instrument panel. (McDonnell Douglas)

its pilots. One possible reason for the few adverse recorded comments about the instrument layout was that it was so much better than what they had had before. But one item did frustrate F86D pilots, and that was the frequent failure of the radar-ranging gunsight to operate at the critical moment. One USAF ace in Korea was quoted as saying, 'I would rather stick a lump of chewing gum on the windscreen.'

The F-4D for the United States Navy was an example of pushing the technology ahead of what was practicable at the time. In the mid 1950s the

'Manta' winged F-4D, particularly the carrier-borne all-weather interceptor version, proved a handful for its pilots because of its far from desirable handling characteristics. The difficulties of the pilot's task were added to by a cockpit whose equipment conformed to no particular ergonomic standard.

The F-4F Phantom was a better pilot's aeroplane. Its cockpit, however, reflected its 1950s origins and very few changes were made throughout a service life of over 30 years.

CHAPTER TEN

HUMAN FACTORS

The primary objective of any study of what we now term human factors, or ergonomics, has always been the improvement of a control position.

With the machines and vehicles of the eighteenth and nineteenth centuries — before powered heavier-than-air flight — little consideration was given to the needs of the human operator, driver, rider or helmsman. Man was expected to adapt to the machine: rarely was the machine adapted to human frailties and physical limitations. Not until the motor car was some thought given by designers to the comfort and well-being of the driver; even then the chauffeur was often seated in the open when the passengers were in a separate enclosed saloon.

Giving due thought to the needs of the human operator does not just mean making sure that he or she can see ahead and can reach the controls. All details such as knobs, levers, wheels, instruments, switches and buttons must be placed in the best position and within view. The seated position adopted must take account of long-term fatigue. Similarly, eye fatigue has to be prevented.

The history of ergonomics in aviation is characterized by a continuous process of looking at why something went wrong and then finding ways to prevent it happening again. Ergonomics has also tried to anticipate problems by extensive research into human factors and particularly into better ways of presenting information to the pilot.

In recent years the subject of human factors has been proposed for inclusion in a pilot's licence examinations. However, only a few airlines, notably KLM which pioneered the idea, include human factors in their training programmes.

Today there are massive volumes in which are to be found most of the answers to the many questions which arise whenever a new flight deck is being designed.

The one thing that runs like a thread throughout the history of man in control of machines and vehicles is the consequence of human error. Human error is always with us. In the history of flying in particular and transport in general, many accidents have been the result of a combination of machine failures and human error. And sometimes human error can be attributed to an error, or errors, on the part of a designer.

Essentially, the useful and descriptive jargon 'man-machine interface' refers to an imaginary boundary which has the aircraft on one side and the pilot on the other. Across this boundary there is a flow of information between the aircraft and the pilot and vice versa. The other important interchange between the two consists of the pilot's actions to control

English Electric Canberra bomber, circa 1950. It is somewhat of a mess, but to be fair we have to remember that in the 1940s, when the design started, neither the instruments nor the equipment were available to effect improvements. Also, the design team had to concentrate on the far greater problems of aerodynamics and structures. Therefore it is understandable that this looks like the cockpit of a Second World War piston-engined bomber rather than that of a jet aircraft.

the aircraft and the movement of the aircraft in response. This is how the pilot perceives the 'feel' of the aircraft.

This interchange of information and actions works perfectly for 99.9 per cent of the time. The aircraft is controlled accurately and the pilot achieves the goal; be it a destination for the passengers or the target for the aircraft's warload. However, on occasions errors are made in the interchange across the control interface. If the design of the controls and instruments fails to match the limitations of the pilot, then this will result in human errors which if not detected in time may result in disaster.

Pilot error, as a verdict, in the first ten years of flying was used to keep up morale. The early aircraft were structurally very weak and their flying characteristics not always adequately explained to novice pilots. The low power of the engine and the drag of the

numerous struts and wires, as well as that of the engine and pilot, meant that, when the engine stopped, the flimsy aircraft, figuratively, also stopped. Unless the pilot pushed the nose down to gain speed in a glide — if that is, there was sufficient height — the aircraft would stall. It followed that it was better for all concerned with aviation that the design deficiencies of aircraft be glossed over and the blame put on the pilot.

In the first fifty years of aviation many accidents were attributed to 'pilot error'. Subsequent experience and hindsight show us that the more correct verdict should have been 'design error'.

In the 1950s and 60s far more attention was given to the relationship between pilot and aircraft, and in particular to the control interface of which the pilot is a primary element. The increase in research into human behaviour when piloting aircraft, and the detailed design of the pilot's place, in these two decades were encouraged by a number of factors, particularly in civil aviation. The consequences of human and mechanical failures were the deaths of crew and passengers. One of the factors was based on a statistic: that over 50 per cent of accidents were attributed to pilot error; another, that aircraft passenger capacity was increasing on average from fifty or so in the early 1950s to a hundred or more, so that one accident could result in a far greater number of fatalities. Also the year-by-year increase in the number of airline passengers carried emphasized the number of incidents and accidents; hence the upsurge in flight deck and cockpit ergonomic studies.

A key factor which had to be considered, and one which still applies, is that a pilot has to make strategic, tactical and managerial decisions within only a few seconds of an event requiring a response. The pilot cannot say, 'Stop, I need to think about the problem'. A command decision has to be an immediate decision.

Instruments form one of the principal elements of the aircraft control interface. As such, they must be designed to prevent reading errors on the part of the pilot. Of all the primary flight instruments the altimeter provides the greatest potential for trouble if it is misread. At night or in cloud the sounds and feel of an aircraft are about the same whether flying at

Another turbine aircraft, the Viscount, whose early versions had flight decks whose style and equipment had been carried over from Second World War bombers. This is an early version of the Vickers Viscount, and an interesting feature is the provision of both toe-operated and hand-operated wheel brakes. Another 'British' feature of this early 1950s turbo-prop airliner is the P-type aperiodic compass with viewing mirror mounted under the overhead of the flight deck. Of particular interest are the exposed rod and crank drives from the electric motors to the windscreen wipers, and the absence of an overhead controls and instrument panel. (Vickers)

10,000 feet or at 1,000 feet. The other instruments do not necessarily give any indication of an aircraft's height.

As the use of pressurized aircraft increased so did the number of incidents and accidents caused primarily through the pilot missreading the altimeter. Pressurized cabins permitted cruising levels well above the 10,000 feet at which most unpressurized aircraft operated. In the interest of passenger comfort, rates of descent in pre-pressurization days rarely exceeded 500 feet per minute. So there was usually time for the crew to appreciate the rate at which height was being lost. But the pressurized airliner, particularly the jets, could descend if need be at 5,000 feet per minute.

The altimeters in general use when pressurized jet aircraft came into regular service were of the three-pointer type.

Typical instrument ergonomics of the late 1940s, including (top centre) the three-pointer altimeter, with its tiny '10,000 feet' pointer, which was to cause so many problems.

The largest pointer indicated hundreds of feet, the larger thousands of feet, and the smallest tens of thousands. These three pointers could easily be missread, particularly at night. Another adverse factor was the crowding of all three pointers and the feet scales, as well as the numeral counters for the barometric setting, into a dial only three inches in diameter.

During a descent from cruising altitude and at times when the crew were concentrating on the complex procedures for entering a controlled traffic zone, they could mentally get out of step with the aircraft — and collectively assume that there was still plenty of height remaining.

Despite the introduction of a 'passing through 10,000' flashing warning light, disasters still occurred in which aircraft hit mountains or flew straight into the ground at night or when descending through cloud. This encouraged the development of the counter-pointer altimeter, and the three-pointer type was then abandoned. The new altimeter, which is still in use, indicates height by means of large numeral counters, with a pointer to indicate the last three digits of the total reading.

Many transport aircraft designed after 1960 were provided with centralized warning systems, and within ten years these became a standard feature on large civil aircraft. A typical system will, by means of an annunciator, flashing light, or illuminated element of a panel, or a combination of these, bring the crew's attention to a particular system. For example, the central warning panel might 'flash up' 'GEN 1'. This tells the crew to attend to the indicators on the electrical generator panel — a panel which may not necessarily be within the crew's normal arcs of vision.

The altimeter is not the only instrument to have caused confusion. Engine instruments have been missread or the readings related to the wrong engine. When a series of accidents to one type of twin-piston-engine aircraft were compared it was realized that a common con-

A counter-pointer altimeter. The numeral counters can read up to 99,900 feet (the pointer indicates the last three digits of the height), and barometric setting is given in both inches of mercury and millibars. This type of instrument was introduced to reduce the number of incidents and accidents arising from '10,000 feet' reading errors. (Smiths Industries)

tributory cause was the shutting down of the 'good' engine instead of the other which was failing. Oil pressure indication for both engines was combined on one instrument. This had two pointers: one for the left and the other for the right engine. Alongside the twin-pointer oil pressure indicator was a similar twin-pointer instrument: this also applied to both engines.

Apparently pilots were looking at the instrument on the right and relating its left-hand pointer to the right-hand engine when in fact the indication of falling oil pressure applied to the left engine. After shutting down the good engine the flight continued on the failing engine until that stopped.

Trajectory

The need for quick reaction to events on the flight deck is underlined by the fact that some 50 per cent of all civil aircraft accidents occur during the approach and landing phases of a flight. During the approach and landing — even in unlimited visibility and calm air — time, distance and events are increasingly compressed as the aircraft nears the touchdown point on the runway. Distance, and the time in which to make corrections, is eaten up at around 250 feet per second. The ability to make corrections to the aircraft's tra-

jectory is also reducing. A large jet aircraft's path cannot be altered quickly, and a few seconds are also needed in which to regain full thrust from the engines.

The pilot of a large jet has therefore to 'aim' the aircraft down a narrow 'funnel', the spout of which is the touchdown point on the runway.

For these reasons the pilot needs clear and unambiguous indications of the aircraft's position, trajectory and 'health'. The advent of more automatic systems has improved the consistency and regularity of landings and has contributed to a reduction of crew workload during critical phases of flight, but automatic systems have not absolved the crew from responsibility and the need to be able to override them and manually fly the aircraft.

Time after time during the evolution of the pilot's place the question has arisen: when and to what extent should the human pilot remain in control. This question is related directly to the quality and amount of information provided by the pilot's view of the real world and that provided by analogues and replicas of the real world, such as instrument displays.

Before considering the information problems during an approach and landing, it is useful to recall the basic variable items of data which the pilot has to interpret, co-ordinate and relate to the instantaneous path of the aircraft. These are: how far the aircraft is to one side of the ideal approach path, which is an extension of the runway centre line; how far the aircraft is above or below the optimum descent path (still called the glide path despite the fact that it is many years since a glide approach by a transport aircraft was possible); the angle made by the aircraft with the approach centre line and with the glide path, and the rate at which the aircraft, if displaced from it, is closing the optimum path.

Any departures from the optimum must be 'zeroed' by the pilot, so that the aircraft arrives on the imaginary line leading to the touchdown point flying at the correct attitude and speed.

When flying manually and relying on the view of the distant runway, the pilot does not have much of a problem, in reasonable visibility conditions, in intercepting the centre line of the approach path and, even in a cross wind, in holding the aircraft to the centre line. But in the vertical plane, a 'visual' landing needs the exercise of considerable judgment and much experience to interpret the perspective view of the approach lights and the apparent shape of the runway. Extreme errors would be obvious to a layman, i.e. much too high on the approach would be readily apparent; much too low and the approach lights and the runway will occupy a very narrow vertical angle. The optimum shape and perspective of the ground features for, say, a three-degree descent path is something which can only be assessed from experience. The difference between the apparent perspective of the runway during a two- or four-degree approach is only marginally dif-

ferent from a three-degree approach. In reduced visibility this task is far more difficult; particularly when the runway threshold appears in the 'picture' only when the aircraft is within a few seconds of touching down. In these conditions a pilot has only these few seconds in which to compare what he can see of the runway with his 'mind's eye' image of the runway. This is why the longest possible view ahead is needed from which to judge height above the runway and when to check the aircraft's rate of descent.

This information element of flight deck design is most critical when the pilot has selected an instrument approach, such as ILS (Instrument Landing System), during which he follows the 'demand' indications of an attitude director (AD) or, in earlier years, a zero reader. At some point on the approach, for example at 300 feet above the runway and 6,000 feet from the touchdown point, which represents about 20 seconds to go, the pilot transfers his attention from the instruments to the view ahead. This transition, which in-

Night Approach. (Rediffusion Simulation Ltd)

cludes re-focussing the eyes to a much longer distance, takes a second or two. Another two or three seconds are needed in which to complete an accurate assessment of the trajectory of the aircraft relative to the desired touchdown point. If the aircraft's attitude, heading, vertical speed and reserve of lift are wrong or inadequate, then another five or six seconds may be needed in which to make all the necessary corrections and for the aircraft to respond.

When ILS was introduced in the 1940s the pilot used the indications of two crossed pointers to keep to the approach path. If the glide-slope pointer was above the fixed symbol representing the aircraft this told the pilot that he was below the glide-slope. If the other, vertical, pointer was over to the right it indicated that the aircraft was to the left of the extended centre line of the runway.

The pointers told the pilot where the aircraft was relative to the two ILS beams. But they did not help him to 'capture' the correct approach path. Only through experience, great concentration and co-ordinating the ILS information with other instruments, could the approach path be smoothly intercepted.

Sperry's zero reader, introduced in 1948, was a sophisticated ILS indicator. It was 'driven' by an electro-mechanical computer which essentially worked on roll and pitch signals from the gyro artificial horizon and on signals from the gyro compass. The two cross lines in the instrument driven by the computer did not necessarily tell the pilot where he was in relation to the required approach path; what they did tell him was in which direction to move the controls. By 'zeroing' the fixed circle, representing the aircraft, on the intersection of the two lines and keeping it there a smooth interception and steady tracking of the approach path would be achieved.

In one step, Sperry eliminated the need to scan and evaluate the separate and different information provided by the gyro artificial horizon, the gyro heading in-

dicator and the gyro compass. One instrument for three!

Within a few years the zero reader was combined with the gyro horizon indicator to form the flight director. This new instrument began to take its place at the top centre position of the Basic Tee. Over the years, and to keep pace with increasing aircraft performance and the need to minimize the pilot's workload, the flight director was further refined. The amount of information afforded the pilot was also considerably increased. It became the attitude director (AD). The modern AD and the horizontal situation (HS) indicator became the primary director instruments of the Basic Tee. The information they provide is very com-

An instrument panel with separate flight instruments for attitude (top centre), ILS (top right) and Sperry Zero Reader (bottom centre) which would eventually be combined in the Attitude Director. These are the second pilot's instruments in an Accountant, circa 1953, an airliner which did not go into production. (Smiths Industries)

Sperry Attitude Director and Horizontal Situation indicators, examples of advanced electro-mechanical instruments. In the 1980s these were being superseded by electronic instrument systems (EIS). (Sperry Flight Systems)

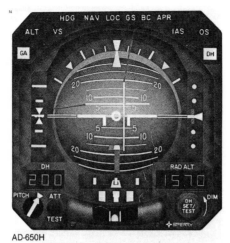

AD-650H

RD-650

Above far right *A British Aerospace Trident airliner on final approach. Neither pilot has his hands on the controls, and the aircraft is being controlled by the automatic landing system. The principal instrument readings are: 140 knots indicated airspeed, altitude 300 feet, vertical speed minus 600 feet per minute. The automatic system also controls the thrust of No 1 and No 3 engine, which is why the throttle of the middle engine is out of line with the others, as are the instrument indications to the right of the white square of the HARCO navigational display. (via Aeroplane Monthly)*

prehensive and illustrations serve far better than words.

During the Second World War, particularly in Britain and the USA, methods were sought of guiding aircraft automatically to a safe touchdown. The RAF wanted a system which would ensure the recovery of large numbers of bombers in reduced visibility.

Development of military automatic landing — autoland — systems continued after the war; especially for the RAF's V-bomber force. The research was eventually extended to include civil passenger-carrying aircraft operations. With approach and landing speeds increasing, sometimes by as much as half, and the need to maintain schedules irrespective of visibility, the development of automatic landing was pushed ahead. At the same time the Royal Aircraft

Establishment (RAE — now Royal Aerospace Establishment) in Britain was perfecting vastly improved systems of approach and runway lighting (e.g. the Calvert). These gave the pilot the maximum guidance during a landing in poor visibility; they began to reduce the number of landing incidents and accidents arising from faster approach speeds and aircraft which were larger and less manoeuvrable.

In 1965 the crew of a British Airways (then British European Airways) Trident airliner let the automatic landing system control the aircraft to a safe landing for the fare-paying passengers on a scheduled flight into London Heathrow.

Autoland required only a few more instruments and controls on the flight deck. Essentially, fully automatic landing was just another step along the road to fully automatic flight. Its origins included the simple auto-rudder control of the Ju52 operating passenger services in the 1930s.

In one important respect, though, automatic landing was a much bigger step than all the others, because it was allowed to maintain control of an aircraft right down to the ground. All the preceeding systems, such as the autopilot, were rarely used below a safe height: a height from which the pilot could take over in the event of a failure.

Automatic landing systems were accepted by pilots and certificated by the authorities responsible for safety because: (1) Their systems were designed so that a failure would not occur more than once in 10 million operations; (2) At any point on the approach and landing, even to within a few feet of touchdown, the pilot was able to disconnect the system and take over himself.

Automatic landing has been developed to such a degree that landings are allowed to continue when runaway visibility is as low as 75 metres. However, once the aircraft is down and decellerating, the pilot has to take over and steer along the centre line until the speed has fallen low enough to allow a safe turn-off onto a taxiway.

Left *Para visual directors (PVDs) in the cockpit of a DH Dove. The 'barber pole' indicators of the PVD are mounted in the coaming above the instrument panel. Similar displays are used in airliners to enable the pilot to track the centre line of the runway following a landing in low visibility. The PVD indicators against the side windows in this research aircraft were used to give pitch commands. (Smiths Industries)*

A Ground Roll Monitor (GRM). Once an airliner has landed, particularly in poor visibility, the pilot needs, in addition to steering guidance from for example PVDs, accurate ground speed and the distance remaining to the end of the runway. (Smiths Industries).

But in 75 metres visibility the pilot does not receive enough visual cues to maintain control. Therefore automatic landing served to add two more instruments to the flight deck. These are the paravisual director (PVD) and the ground roll monitor (GRM). The PVD operates on signals received from the instrument landing system localizer beam directed along the centre of the runway and from a system of gyros. It produces 'barber's pole' indicators whose stripes 'stream' to the left or right. The pilot follows their indications to keep to the centre line of the runway. The GRM indicates ground speed in knots and distance to go to the end of the runway in metres, information being fed via sensors on the main wheels.

Requirements

Each nation issues a set of airworthiness requirements which includes specifying the minimum number and position of instruments. In Europe there is an agreed set of joint requirements which are generally similar to those of the USA.

The requirements specify, for example, that the primary flight in-

struments must be clearly visible to the pilot with the minimum practicable deviation from his normal seated position, and when looking forward along the flight path.

Also specified is the Basic Tee configuration for airspeed, altitude, attitude and navigation displays and the use of the colour red for warnings, amber for caution and green for safe operation.

The requirements also take into account that there may be failures among the instrument systems. Those primary instruments in front of the first pilot (captain) must therefore have an alternative information source.

The minimum set of instruments required for a civil passenger transport are, in front of each pilot: airspeed, Mach number, altimeter, vertical speed, rate of turn and slip/skid, bank and pitch angles as well as heading. Both pilots must be able to see, without leaving their seats, instruments displaying outside air temperature, time and a stand-by direction indicator. In practice, flight decks are usually equipped with a third set of primary flight instruments.

In turbo-prop and turbo-jet aircraft the list of required engine instruments includes, for each engine: fuel pressure warning, oil quantity, oil pressure warning, oil temperature, fire warning, turbine exhaust gas temperature, fuel flow rate, shaft speed and ice protection. Fuel tank contents indication is another important requirement.

Such requirements represent only a small part of the total number of instruments and indicators on the flight deck. Navigation, communication, aircraft systems management and health, passenger comfort through control of the cabin environment, and emergency systems — all need instruments and controls.

Of course, the flight deck crew does not have to scan continuously all the instruments and check all the controls throughout a flight. The most frequently used, which are also the most important instruments and controls, are placed in

How many on the flight deck?

The two-pilot, side-by-side, flight deck arrangement has been an international standard since about 1935. However, large aircraft and in particular aircraft operating transoceanic flights, tended, until the 1950s, to carry a crew of two pilots, navigator, flight engineer and radio operator. The navigator was sometimes a pilot. These large crew complements were necessary because of the need for specialists to concentrate on managing the navigation, including taking 'star shots' for astro-navigation, monitoring the engines and fuel system and communicating over long distances.

That is a generalization, in that for a given aircraft there have been many variations in crew complement among the world's airlines. For example, a DC3 operating internal 'on the beam' flights in the USA needed only two pilots to fly it, manage its systems, navigate and communicate. However, were the same aircraft to be operated over oceans and away from an airways system of beams and beacons, then both a navigator and a radio operator might have had to be carried. If a four-engine aircraft, such as the DC4 series, were operated on transoceanic routes, then in addition to a navigator and radio operator a flight engineer might be carried. The engineer would occupy the 'jump' seat abaft the central control pedestal because there was no separate engine and systems panel.

Examples abound to demonstrate that the size and qualifications of a flight deck crew have not always been directly related to the type of aircraft. It has continued to be a case more of 'horses for courses'.

The Basic T instrument layout in an HS 125 jet. (British Aerospace)

front of the pilots and within reach of their hands. Those of lesser importance are located to one side of their forward arcs of vision.

The flight deck of a Tupelov 134. Russian civil aircraft design often included a forward navigator's station; this required a gangway through the main instrument panel, so the throttle pedestals had to be at the sides. Russian flight decks were at one time very different from those in the West. Here, the cooling fans are not usually found outside Russia. The pilots enjoyed extensive upward view transparencies. (Smiths Industries)

Aircraft weight has been used as the measure of crew complements. For example, in the early 1950s an aircraft of 80,000 lb and over all-up-weight had to have three crew members on the flight deck. Even a particular airline's desire to avoid an additional 'union' on the flight deck, i.e. a flight engineer, influenced the design and equipment of the flight deck — as with the Vanguard for British European Airways.

The gradual elimination of the specialist navigator is the result of the steady improvement in the number, range and quality of electronic aids — such as radio beacons (VORs) and distance measuring equipment (DME). By the end of the 1940s the primary navigational task was no longer that of 'where are we?', or even of how to get to a

destination, but how to get there along a path, which could be indirect, as defined by air traffic control.

The navigation of an aircraft was no longer an intermittent process. In place of checking position at intervals and updating the navigation plot, positional information was available from electronic aids on a continuous basis. More importantly it did not have to be interpreted or processed by a navigator. The pilots could read the information on their panel-mounted instruments.

Contributing to the subject of 'how many on the flight deck?' is the inertial navigation system, or INS. This self-contained system of accelerometers, gyroscopes and computer continuously displays aircraft position in latitude and longitude. It answers the question 'Where are we?' and as with DECCA and similar aids replaces the special skills of the human navigator.

By about 1965 the pressure of minimum operating costs induced airlines to limit crews to two pilots only, whenever the regulations allowed and the pilots' unions agreed. The airlines argued that provided all the vital instruments were arranged to be within the vision arcs of both pilots and all the essential controls were within their reach, then two pilots were sufficient irrespective of the all-up weight of the aircraft. The pilots argued strongly that safety was being compromised by increasing workload and, in the event of one of the pilots being incapacitated, the other would be overloaded beyond a safe limit. They were particularly concerned over 'multiple events', such as one pilot unconscious or injured, a major mechanical fault such as an engine failing, plus marginal visibility and inadequate landing aids at the nearest and possibly only suitable airport.

Acceptance of the two-pilot only and two-pilot plus flight engineer flight deck arrangements for transport aircraft gained ground in the 1960s because the employment prospects of pilots were not adversely affected. The flight (systems) engineers, like the radio operators and navigators before them, became industrially weaker as their numbers dwindled. The flight engineer has survived the longest, most of the larger transport aircraft having a systems panel and flight engineer's seat separate from the controls and instruments used by the pilots.

In the late 60s both Boeing and Lockheed developed large aircraft (B747 and L1011) with flight decks arranged for two pilots plus a systems engineer. Eventually the Boeing 747, the dash 400 version of 1988, would have a two-pilot only flight deck despite a maximum weight of over 400 tons and a range of 7,000 miles; albeit accommodation would be provided for a relief crew.

Another factor put forward by those who favoured reducing the number of a flight crew was the significant reduction in flight times afforded by the jets which replaced the piston-engine aircraft.

Increasingly then, during the 1970s new aircraft and up-dated versions of existing types entered service with two-pilot only flight decks, and to some extent the crew complement controversy tended to abate.

CHAPTER ELEVEN

DESIGNING THE PILOT'S PLACE

VC10, circa 1965: a well-appointed, well-fenestrated and neatly arranged flight deck. (Smiths Industries).

Pilot opinion

If a dozen pilots were asked to give an opinion on the merits or disadvantages of a particular cockpit, they would be more than likely to come up with as many answers. The same would probably happen if they were asked to name their ideal aircraft.

Pilot opinion is no more quantifiable than that of any other particular profession. Judgements expressed on a cockpit and its equipment are far from being the outcome of a scientific process. They are more likely to be the result of subjective impressions. Much depends on the attitude of individuals and their particular preferences based on their years of experience. One pilot may damn an aircraft without further comment; another may be lavish in praise of the same type.

Perhaps the only true measure of the qualities of an aircraft and of its pilot's place in particular is the record of incidents and accidents. If an item of control equipment has contributed to a significant number of errors, near accidents and destructive accidents, then the aviation equivalent of the 'man in the street' or 'they' will produce a statement with which all pilots are agreed.

Once a pilot becomes used to the handling characteristics of an aircraft, however vicious some might be, the most

Modern transport aircraft flight deck dimensions. (Author)

lasting impression is that of the working environment of the cockpit.

After a few hours, any bad ergonomics leave a distinct mental and physical impression. The uncomfortable seat and harness and the controls placed out of reach were often accepted by fighter pilots when each of the sorties they flew amounted to only an hour or two and when destroying the enemy and surviving were more than enough to occupy their thoughts during that time. But when flights exceed two hours then discomfort begins to dominate the pilot's actions and to imprint a lasting impression on his recollections (if not on his gluteus maximus) of that particular type of aircraft.

Criteria

For transport aircraft, the basic criteria to have emerged for improved cockpit design — for an efficient man-machine interface, for limiting human workload and for reducing the risk of incidents, failures and disasters to a minimum — includes the following:

1. An adjustable and comfortable seat for each flight deck crew position.
2. A good all-round view in the horizontal plane, including a view of the wing tip outboard of each pilot's seat.
3. A downward view over the nose of

the aircraft so that when making a visual approach to a landing a sufficient length of approach lighting is visible.

4. An upward view for use when the aircraft is banked in a turn.

5. All primary and secondary controls, selectors, adjusters and switches to be within reach of the pilot's hands without the need to stretch. Each pilot to be able to visually cross-check the primary flight instruments in front of the other pilot.

6. Each pilot to be able to control the aircraft without having to change seats.

For single-seat military aircraft, the principal design criteria clearly also relates to the offensive, defensive and reconnaissance roles of a fighter-attack aircraft. Dominating the design process for the military aircraft cockpit is the 'trade-

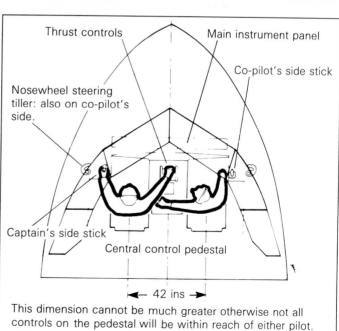

This dimension cannot be much greater otherwise not all controls on the pedestal will be within reach of either pilot.

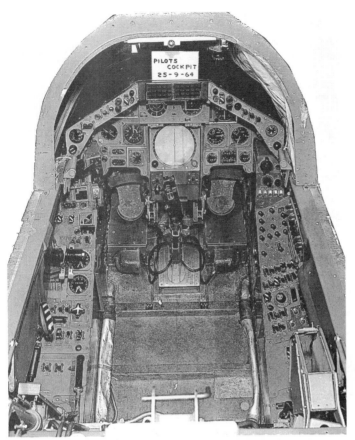

BAC TSR2 front cockpit, circa 1964. Considerable attention was paid to ergonomic requirements, and the cockpit incorporated many new instrument ideas. But 25 years or more later, the lack of electronic displays emphasizes the progress which has been made since TSR2 was consigned by the politicians to the scrap heap. (British Aerospace)

and workload-reducing control interface is so important that every item, however small, has to have its importance and frequency of use accurately weighed before taking its place among the others.

Not all these items can be sited in the optimum location because of the physical limitations of the cockpit structure, the ejection seat and the canopy. And also because of the natural limitations of the pilot's hands and limbs. For example, the designer had to avoid placing too many controls for operation by one particular hand.

In order to simplify the description of a modern fighter/attack cockpit the various items can be grouped as follows:
1) information and display (including radar and other sensor data)
2) control
3) communication

Each of these main groupings of instruments, selector switches, levers and keypads as well as warning and attention-getting lights can be subdivided. The majority are concerned with avionic systems, which is not surprising since about one third of the cost of an aircraft is accounted for by the various electronic systems. Why so many avionic systems? Part of the answer is because at least the following have to be included to enable the pilot and aircraft to operate as an effective weapon system:

flight management and control
navigation, target acquisition and identification
communication
weapon-aiming and management
defensive electronics such as tail warning radar, decoy flares and electronic jamming

As the design of an aircraft proceeds from stage to stage the list of avionics and other systems affecting the design of the cockpit expands. Because modern single-seat and two-seat combat aircraft are often classified as 'multi-role', then the number of systems is obviously going to be greater than those for a limited role type.

off' between a number of conflicting requirements imposed not least by limitations of space. The designer has therefore to be prepared to cut drastically into a long list of cockpit items by asking the questions: what items are essential and what items can be discarded without affecting the efficient functioning of the control interface? What does the pilot need to know about? Even if certain information were provided could the pilot use it?

With over a hundred instruments, lights, indicators, switches, buttons and levers to be included, considerable thought has to be given to the fighter-attack aircraft cockpit. Fifty years ago cockpit items were allocated positions using such design criteria as mechanical convenience and the availability of a convenient part of the cockpit structure as a mounting. Today an effective, efficient

The 'basic' cockpit is that of the trainer aircraft, which does not necessarily have to include offensive and defensive systems controls and instruments. However, some trainer aircraft have limited 'combat' avionic systems to ensure that the pilot's graduation from trainer to front-line combat aircraft is as small a step as practicable.

The Hawk series from British Aerospace provides a good example of a range of cockpits to match different aircraft roles within a basic airframe and cockpit: from the RAF trainer version, with its comparatively simple cockpit, to the Hawk 100 and 200 which have head-up display and weapon-aiming systems for use with offensive equipment.

Compared with flying the second generation of jet fighters (F86 and Hunter

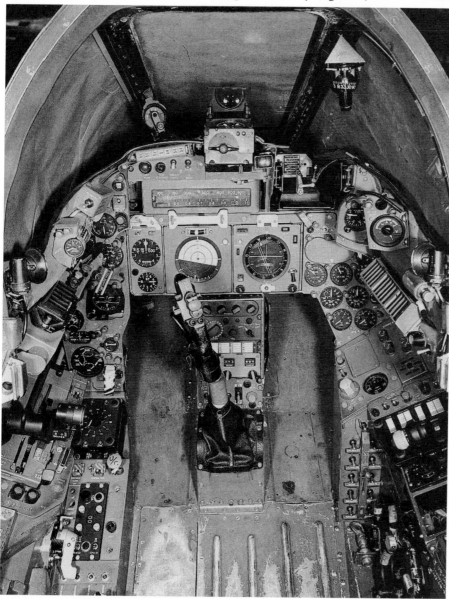

English Electric Lightning, circa 1965. This formidable and long-serving RAF interceptor was equipped with the latest in primary flight instruments. These included: two horizontal tape display of airspeed (knots) and Mach number; attitude director and horizontal situation indicators side-by-side rather than one above the other (a departure from the arrangement to which the RAF had adhered for over 25 years); and altimeter and vertical speed indicator moved over to the left of the panel. The Lightning arrived too early to be equipped with an electronic head-up display (HUD), and it may not have been possible to effect a retrospective installation because of the lack of space at the base of the windscreen. Therefore the pilot had to make do with a gyro reflector sight. (British Aerospace)

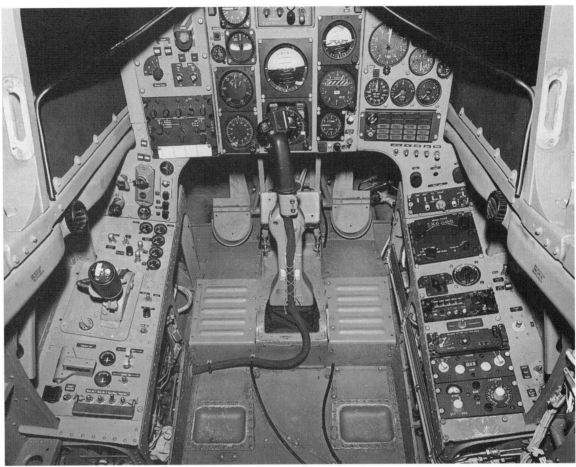

The front cockpit of a British Aerospace Hawk trainer. Apart from the absence of weapon-aiming systems, this could be a front-line fighter — later versions of the Hawk were equipped with weapons. Unlike earlier generation trainers, the Hawk is well equipped with communication systems. (British Aerospace)

for example) the combat aircraft pilot of the 1990s is given far more information. Pilots of the earliest jets had to devote time to managing many of the aircraft systems. They had to watch closely the rate at which fuel was being used and at intervals select different fuel tanks to maintain trim; watch the engine instruments whenever they moved the thrust lever to ensure that they did not overstress the engine or cause it to surge or flame-out; 'eyeball' the target, because there were few if any electronic devices to help with acquiring and identifying a target; and keep a visual lookout for hostile aircraft, because there were few electronic warning systems and no electronic countermeasures.

If the first-generation jet pilots had to fly at low level, they had to concentrate

on the view ahead to avoid hitting the ground. There was no such thing as terrain-following radar or a height warning radar altimeter. When aiming at the target they had to concentrate on the graticule of the gyro gunsight; at the same time feeding target range to the ballistic computer, using the twist grip on the end of the throttle lever. All this meant that during critical phases of a flight the pilot had no time in which to look down at the cockpit instrument panel.

Essentially the avionics, which now 'fill' the cockpit with so many displays and controls, are there to make sure that the modern fighter/attack aircraft pilot can fly it in all visibility conditions, can avoid hostile detection devices and missiles, can reach the target, and can find and destroy the target with a high

probability of success and also get home safely.

Pilot's equipment

Much of the equipment, such as instruments and controls, on the flight deck of a transport aircraft and in the cockpit of a fast jet military machine may be similar. However, one item is completely different: the pilot's personal equipment, and in particular the headgear.

The transport pilot wears, when necessary, a lightweight headset with small boom microphone. A lightweight, quick-action, oxygen mask is always close to hand. In contrast the pilot of an air force jet is 'close mewed up' in a heavy helmet.

The close affinity of pilot and aircraft

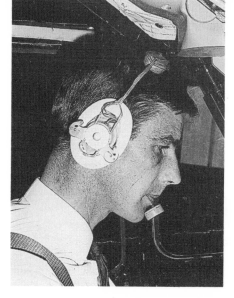

Above *The instructor's cockpit of a Hawk trainer.* (British Aerospace)

Left *Lightweight communications headset worn by a transport aircraft pilot.* (Smiths Industries)

Right *Combating G. The pilot's seat is inclined 60 degrees from the vertical, but this introduces the problem of space and the need to make the primary control stick and throttle part of the two-position seat.* (Author)

Below *RAF Harrier GR3 pilots aboard HMS Ark Royal. They are wearing one-piece flotation and survival suits incorporating anti-G pressurizing elements.* (Crown Copyright)

has been a characteristic of flying since the pioneering days, when the feel of the machine and the slipstream striking the pilot's face were important 'instrumental' aids to control. When cockpits were enclosed, pilots became to some extent isolated from the aircraft and the air through which they flew. The pilot came to depend more and more on the readings of the instruments.

With the advent of the jet engine and with sealed, pressurized and air-conditioned cockpits the pilot was further isolated; yet, paradoxically, he became even more a part of the aircraft once ejection seats were introduced into military aircraft: he was now securely fastened and restrained by the complicated seat harness, and the aircraft was a more immediate extension of his body.

In the days when aircraft had top speeds of less than 100 mph, and sometimes very much less, pilots were able to climb aboard and take off wearing their normal clothing or uniform; a concession to the cold air might be a pair of driving gloves, some string round the ankles, a peaked cap worn back to front and goggles. Once the First World War got into its stride pilots took to wearing fleece-lined flying suits — the Sidcot, for example. In the final year of the war electrically-heated garments were available.

Seventy years ago the fighter cockpit, as far as the pilot was concerned, consisted of a simple, non-adjustable seat, a seat harness and, if he was especially favoured, a parachute. Apart from a Sidcot one-piece flying suit and a helmet, little else was devoted to his safety and comfort. Eventually oxygen systems were added and parachutes became the rule rather than the exception.

The cumbersome crash helmets affected by the pioneer aviators gave way to lined, soft leather flying helmets which could be fastened under the chin. With the addition of Gosport voice pipes or intercom earphones and oxygen masks the soft helmet remained in use until after the coming of the jet age.

For the first 50 years of aviation pilots were able to bend, turn their heads and reach around; their only constraint was the safety harness. However, the need to conserve a pilot's faculties in the high G environment of the jet meant that he had to wear an anti-G garment as well as flame resistant overalls — which also gave protection against extremes of temperature should he have to eject and then land in the sea. Added to the constriction of the seat and leg restraint harness was the 'bone dome' helmet, which limited head movement and whose weight was multiplied by G effects. The shirt-sleeve environment of some 1940s cockpits was swept away by the extreme effects of flying jets and the difficulties of surviving.

The advent of in-flight refuelling for jet strike/fighter aircraft made possible sorties and transoceanic ferry flights in which the pilot is confined to his seat for half a day or longer. Swaddled in his survival suit, anti-G gear and heavy helmet, as festooned with leads and all the other things needed to keep him alive, alert and well, the pilot has to be very fit and have great stamina. Why the heavy, complex helmets for pilots of high-performance military aircraft? Apart from protecting the skull in the event of having to eject or make a crash landing, without such a helmet he would be unable to hear, let alone understand, radio information; would have nothing on which to secure the oxygen mask; and no protection

against the extremely high noise level in the cockpit of a fast jet. The disadvantages? As well as the load the helmet imposes on the pilot's neck, it also restricts head movement, except over the forward arcs-of-view.

Ejecting

Getting out of an aircraft in a hurry has not always been as easy as the *Pilot's Notes* might suggest. There was always the chance of a hang-up of some sort. With the high-performance jet aircraft of the mid-forties and thereafter it was essential to give the pilot every possible bit of help.

The first aircraft to be fitted with an ejection seat was the Heinkel 280 twin-jet fighter for the German air force. This was as early as 1940 and predates the ejection seats of Britain and America by at least five years. The next Heinkel jet, the

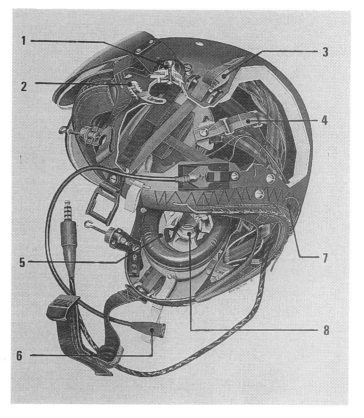

Modern combat pilot's helmet. 1 Friction controlled visor hinges; 2 Adjustable clear visor lock plate; 3 Headset tensioning straps and buckles; 4 Rear cross webbing buckles; 5 Noise suppressing capsules and PVC seals; 6 Oxygen mask microphone connector; 7 Fore and aft diagonal webbing cord; 8 Miniature receivers (Helmets Ltd)

Right *Dornier 335, circa 1944, one engine pulling and the other pushing. This arrangement set a number of problems for the designer in providing for the safe escape of the pilot.* (via Aeroplane Monthly)

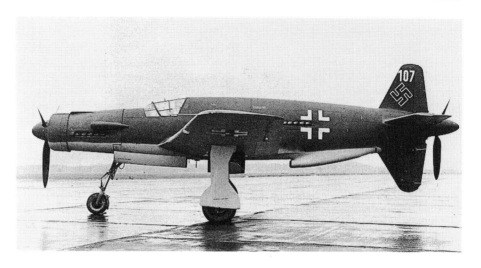

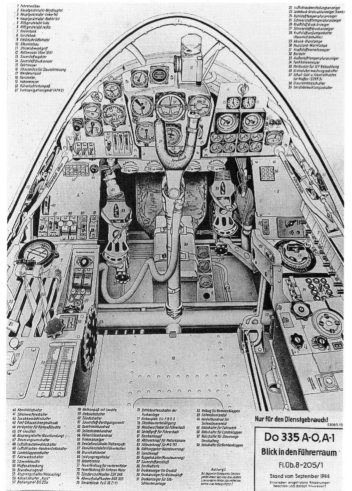

Nur für den Dienstgebrauch!

Do 335 A-O, A-1
Blick in den Führerraum

Fl.Üb.8-205/1

Stand vom September 1944

He162, also featured an ejection seat. However, this was 'fired' by a cartridge and not by compressed air as in the 280. Surprisingly, the one German jet fighter used operationally, the Me262, did not have an ejection seat and neither did the fearsome rocket-propelled Me163.

Two piston-engine/propeller aircraft were equipped with ejection seats. The Dornier 335, one engine pulling, the other pushing, had three emergency buttons in the cockpit: the first initiated the charge which blew off the aft propeller; the second actuated another charge which got rid of the upper tail fin, and the third button armed the ejection seat. Only then could the pilot manually release the canopy, followed by — if any time remained — squeezing the firing trigger in the armrest of the seat.

The other was the He219A twin-engine night fighter, in which both pilot and radar operator were given compressed air operated ejection seats: skilled aircrew, like fuel, were in short supply in the last two years of the Second World War.

When parachutes were first supplied as squadron standard, room was usually found for the pack by taking out the pilot's seat cushion. Thirty years later the equivalent of the parachute in life-saving terms, the ejection seat, could not be fitted retrospectively to all aircraft. An ejection seat is a fairly massive item for which space must be allocated when the aircraft is on the drawing board.

The Meteor Mk.8 was the first RAF aircraft to be equipped with a production Martin Baker ejection seat. This was in 1950. Earlier versions of the Meteor were no better equipped for baling out than were contemporary piston-engined fighters. Although the Mk.8 had an ejection seat, subsequent versions of the Meteor did not necessarily have this valuable saver of pilot's lives: the NF11 and Meteor 12s and 14s were without them.

The Hunter was designed from the start for an ejection seat, the Mk.2 having the fully automatic seat which would complete all sequential actions without the intervention of the pilot: if he lost consciousness after triggering the seat, his harness would be automatically released at the right moment and his parachute deployed.

Just as parachutes were available to the RAF in its first few years but were not considered essential except, that is, by pilots, so ejection seats were available when the V-bomber series for the RAF was on the drawing board. But only for the pilots, not for the other crew members. A pilot sitting in his ejection seat and knowing that the other crew members also have ejection seats will not hesitate to eject. The two pilots of, say, a Vulcan were placed in the invidious position of knowing not only that they must delay their own escape to allow the others to bale out through the lower hatch, but that a conventional parachute exit from a high-performance jet is not always successful.

The horrific injuries leading to death sustained by aircrew ejecting from an aircraft flying at over 600 knots prompted the design of individual escape capsules for the three-man crew of the B58 Hustler Mach 2 bomber of the USAF. In the event of trouble, the pilot, navigator and electronics officer of the B58 pulled one of two pre-ejection sequence handles. These

initiated closure of a 'lobster back' capsule which extended over and down in front of his seat. The capsule was pressurized automatically before the cockpit canopy was blown off by an explosive charge. Another charge then fired the capsule out of the aircraft. A parachute was used to lower the capsule to the ground.

An interesting feature of the pilot's capsule in the B58 was the window which provided a view of the main instrument panel. There was also a control column inside the capsule which enabled the pilot to maintain control of the aircraft until the crew had escaped or until the aircraft

Below far left *Dornier 335 cockpit. The tube attached to the two-handed stick is part of the oxygen supply system, and the ejection seat trigger bracket extends upward from the right front corner of the seat.* (via Aeroplane Monthly)

Below *A modern ejection seat.* (Martin Baker)

had descended to a lower altitude. Indeed, a very costly and complex system, but one which the USAF considered absolutely essential.

The prototype of the USAF's B1 long-range supersonic bomber development of which started in the early 1970s, did not have individual ejections seats. Instead the pressurized module which housed the crew could be separated by controlled explosions. Once clear of the aircraft a group of parachutes could be deployed to slow the crew module's descent. A similar crew escape and recovery system was developed for the F111 bomber.

In the B1 the dilemma faced by the Vulcan's pilots, of hesitating to save their lives by ejecting to leave the other three crew members to make a conventional parachute exit, should not arise. But when the B1 was at the prototype stage there was uncertainty over who should trigger the escape module ejection. At first the system was arranged so that any crew member could initiate the ejection sequence. A warning light in front of the pilots alerted them to the pending abandonment of the aircraft if one of the system operators pulled their ejection handle. However the pilots could override the sequence. Later the ejection circuits were changed so that it would require the simultaneous operation of both systems operators' ejection handles to 'fire off' the escape module but the pilots would not be able to override the crew members' decision. However, all uncertainty was overcome by abandoning the escape module principle and instead having individual ejection seats for the crew members.

Another example of special 'escape' design was the jettisonable nose section and cockpit of the Russian SU–17 of 1949.

Both the escape module and the ejection seat reflect the speed with which events occur following an engine failure, fire and explosion or structural damage.

At low altitude only two or three seconds remain in which to get clear. At high altitude both ejection seats and escape capsules include the necessary life support services.

The heavy head

The Grumman F14 twin-engine, twin-fin fighter of the United States Navy is in a near vertical climb. With plenty of speed before pulling up and with full thrust the F14 will go on climbing. However there are circumstances when an F14 pilot may find his aircraft in the same nose-high attitude but with insufficient speed. This can occur when manoeuvring to stay on the tail of another aircraft during combat.

Beyond a nose-up angle of about 20 degrees the F14 becomes unstable: the pilot finds that the nose yaws from side to side. As the angle increases, the wings begin to rock. The controls even reverse: moving the stick to the right to try and counteract the roll to the left may not have the desired effect; the left roll increases.

If during combat an F14 slides off its tail into a spin it will start to rotate at over 150 degrees per second; in other words it makes a complete turn in about two seconds. The pilot becomes disorientated. Even worse, the pilot, who is seated about 20 feet ahead of the centre of rotation, is pressed forward by a 5-G load: his neck is trying to resist the combined weight of his head and helmet, which is now over 200lb.

In such G-loads the pilot finds it virtually impossible to use his hands to operate the controls. With his body strained forward against the harness and his neck stretched fully out he can be severely injured if he attempts to fire his ejection seat.

This is an extreme case but it serves to illustrate and emphasize that fighter cockpit design and pilot's equipment and ejector seat for the 1990s have to meet a stringent set of conditions.

CHAPTER TWELVE

THE PILOT'S PLACE IN THE 70s AND 80s

Perfection?

One hundred per cent perfection is rarely obtainable in any form of transport, but within the limits of the available technology for controls and instruments the 1970s flight deck was far advanced ergonomically from the control positions of the 1950s.

Flight decks of the 70s exhibited few error-inducing switches, levers and instruments compared with earlier years. A vast fund of data gathered by medical specialists, psychologists and ergonomists became the basis of clearly defined criteria for the shape, position, colour and presentation of controls and instruments; it also formed the basis of sound design for the interrelationship between different items of control and display on the flight deck of a transport aircraft.

However, this 'golden' ergonomic decade coincided with a number of new factors which eventually introduced many important changes to the transport aircraft flight deck. These were: an upward jump in the price of fuel which necessitated new fuel-saving flight techniques; increasing pressure to reduce other costs by limiting the flight crew to two pilots only; and the recognition that these factors predicated an overall improvement to the man-machine interface,

the flight deck, in order to limit and even reduce the workload on the pilots. One outcome was the increasing use of integrated computer-based systems for the control and management of an aircraft.

By the 1980s — by 1985 at any rate — the civil transport flight deck was changed; not out of recognition but in more subtle ways. A 1960s pilot who had slept for 25 years before waking at the controls of an A320 Airbus would quickly grasp what was what. But at the same time he would be in a very different overall environment. There would also be a considerable number of different operating techniques.

Whereas some 30 years ago the pilot took decisions and then initiated action by operating a control, today's pilot lets the digital computer systems get on with flying the aircraft. The electronic displays provide a comprehensive 'picture' of how the aircraft is performing and the health of all its systems. Having been given the facts and a waypoint or destination, the computers can be left to fly the aircraft.

Perhaps one of the big differences between the flight deck of the 1980s, and that of earlier decades is the amount of immediately available 'future' information. In place of the time-consuming use of charts, performance tables and mechanical no-memory computers, the pilot has instant predictions available on

Electronic head-up display in the cockpit of an RAF Harrier. The combining glass which, as it implies, combines the pilot's view ahead with electronically generated symbols and alphanumerics, is the sloping glass above the 'crash' pad. The HUD controls are on a long narrow vertical panel on the left. In later designs of HUD the control panel is integral with the display unit. (Smiths Industries)

where the aircraft will be in three-dimensional space and how much fuel will remain at some selectable time in the future.

The flight deck crews of today also have the benefit of the extensive use of colour to differentiate among the different displays, symbols and alphanumerics. Colour provides the means to emphasize or call attention to malfunctions and adverse trends. For example: yellow to indicate that a particular system needs attending to, or red as a warning that immediate action must be taken.

The extensive use of electronic technology — aviation electronics, or avionics — has brought about a transformation of the pilot's place; its contribu-

tion to civil aviation has been to make possible acceptable standards of performance and safety, and economy of operation.

Fighter effectiveness

A modern combat aircraft, its structure, engines, instruments and controls, its avionics and the pilot, together make up a weapon system. To make the most effective use of this system requires sophisticated methods of acquiring and aiming at targets.

The cockpits of two particular air force aircraft have an important place in the history of the pilot's place. These are the Buccaneer and the Harrier, developed in

Pilot's display unit (PDU) of the head-up display and weapon-aiming systems (HUDWAS) in the Harrier AV-8B of the USMC and the RAF. The up-front control panel is integral with the display unit. (Smiths Industries)

the early 1960s. Both were among the first to be equipped with an electronic 'head-up' display (HUD) in place of the gyro, lead-computing, gun sights. The first HUDs had analogue computers, but within a few years the digital computer arrived and HUD versatility, reliability and performance were significantly improved.

The HUD, with its large sloping combining glass set in the pilot's forward line-of-sight, has become a dominating feature of the cockpits of modern fighter/attack aircraft. It enables the pilot to concentrate on the target, be it in the air or on the ground, without having to glance down at the conventional instruments in order to check the following: attitude, heading, speed, vertical speed; angle-of-attack, altitude, weapon status and selection and other vital items of information. The symbols and alphanumerics of the display are projected from a CRT through a system of lens and superimposed on the pilot's view ahead. The lens system collimates the images so that they are focused at infinity. Part of the symbology provides weapon-aiming.

Within limits the software/data base of an HUD computer can generate a wide range of information sets to match different aircraft operating modes: air-to-air combat, ground and ship attack, en-route navigation and recovery to base. The data base and the sensors which provide inputs to the system can be extended to include displays of information concerning engine health, fuel status and radio frequencies.

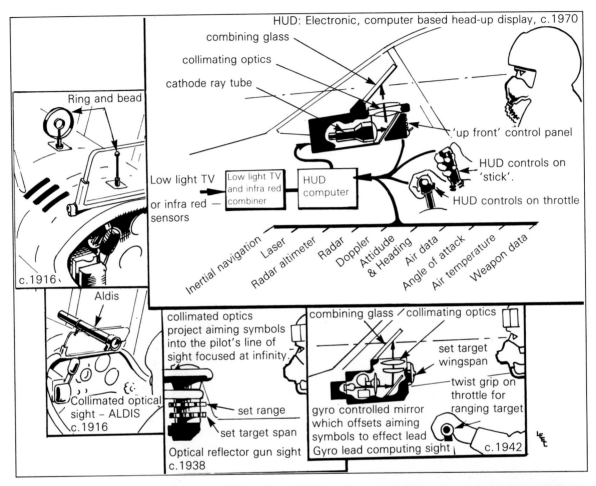

HUD: Electronic, computer based head-up display, c.1970

combining glass

collimating optics

cathode ray tube

Ring and bead

'up front' control panel

HUD controls on 'stick'.

Low light TV

Low light TV and infra red combiner

HUD computer

HUD controls on throttle

or infra red — sensors

c.1916

Inertial navigation   Laser   Radar altimeter   Radar   Doppler   Attitude & Heading   Air data   Angle of attack   Air temperature   Weapon data

Aldis

collimated optics project aiming symbols into the pilot's line of sight focused at infinity.

combining glass / collimating optics

set target wingspan

twist grip on throttle for ranging target

Collimated optical sight – ALDIS
c.1916

set range

set target span

gyro controlled mirror which offsets aiming symbols to effect lead
Gyro lead computing sight

c.1942

Optical reflector gun sight
c.1938

Above *The evolution of head-up display, from ring and bead to electronic HUD and weapon aiming.* (Author)

Right *Multi-function electronic display unit with in map mode.* (Ferranti)

In the early 1980s colour CRT multi-function displays (MFDs) were introduced for military aircraft. These complement the HUD and are used to display a number of different sets of data, as selected by the pilot, using the 'soft keys' mounted along the sides of the display unit. For example, during the flight towards a target the pilot can select a map presentation which gives an instant check on position and progress, ground contours and colour-differentiated heights as well as the location of hostile missile and radar areas.

Other selectable displays include system status. For example, by selecting 'FUEL' the pilot sees a diagrammatic representation of the aircraft's complete fuel system including drop tanks. Each

FERRANTI

tank symbol includes an indication of the quantity remaining, and each valve and pump symbol shows the status of the item, i.e. OPEN, CLOSED, ON, OFF.

For the greater part of a sortie the pilot need only refer to the HUD and the MFD and the up-front control/selector panel mounted just below the display head of the HUD.

A further refinement in the modern fighter/attack cockpit is the concept of HOTAS (hands on throttle and stick). This means what its acronym indicates because, for the majority of a flight, and particularly during combat or attack, the pilot is able to control the aircraft and to select all vital functions and systems without taking the left hand off the throttle and the right-hand off the stick.

Over the years, the throttle lever and the control column — the stick — have acquired more and more switches and buttons. They are no longer, as in simpler times, a lever or hand grip with one or two buttons. They now sprout a large panel on the hand grip on which to mount an array of buttons, switches and small levers for use by all ten of the pilot's fingers.

A 1980s fighter-attack aircraft control column may have as many as a dozen switches and buttons and the throttle lever another eight or more.

Pressurization

The introduction of pressurization, particularly for civil aircraft, imposed severe limitations on the area of the flight deck

Improving the Harrier: the Royal Aerospace Establishment's 'Nightbird'. In addition to the head-up display there is a forward looking infra-red (FLIR) display below the HUD and an electronic map display unit. These units are integrated with a video tape recorder and an inertial navigation system. (Ferranti)

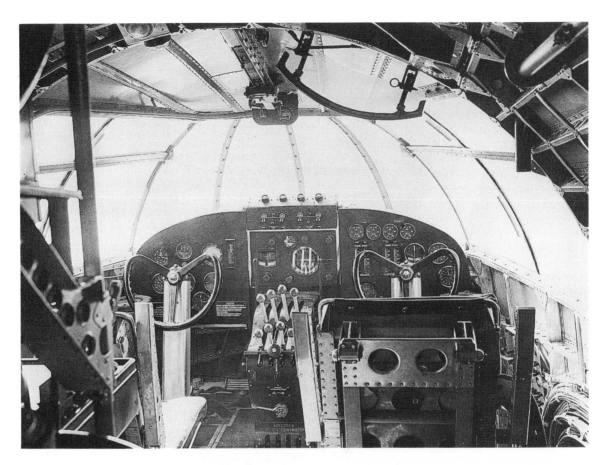

An unpressurized flight deck of the 1930s as a comparison in fields-of-view. (via Aeroplane Monthly)

windows. Reduced arcs-of-view meant that the chances of failing to spot another aircraft on a collision course increased. Readers are reminded that the human eye quickly detects moving objects but is less able to spot those which are stationary. An aircraft on a collision course has no apparent movement relative to the observer.

Pressurized transport aircraft entered service in increasing numbers in the mid-1940s. This particular advance in aviation coincided with a large increase in the numbers of aircraft using the airways. One result was an increase in the probability of mid-air collisions. Avionic systems were therefore added to meet the demand for more accurate track keeping.

Until about 1950 the majority of civil transports cruised at about 250 knots. Within a mere ten years jet propulsion pushed cruising speeds to 400 knots or more. Still more accurate electronic aids were needed to ensure that the optimum tracks and flight profiles (climbs, cruising levels and descents) were flown to take the maximum advantage of the jet engine; as part of a process of cause and effect, the development of new avionic systems had to keep pace with increased speeds and operating heights. In the 1960s there was an even greater upsurge in air traffic and in consequence more avionics were needed, particularly on the flight deck, in order to make the most effective and safe use of the airways systems.

We have seen how the civil transport flight deck evolved during the 1930s and how the two-pilot, side-by-side arrangement became the international standard. Compared with a tandem pilot position this conferred the important advantage that the majority of the controls and instruments could be operated and monitored by the two pilots. And most importantly it was not necessary to duplicate engine and systems control levers and switches. Of course, vital — that is, essential — systems and instruments are duplicated and often triplicated so that in the event of a failure the crew will not be deprived completely of control or information. In contrast, less multiplication is acceptable in a combat aircraft because in the last resort the crew can eject.

In addition to the avionics concerned directly with the control and navigation of an aircraft there are a number of other systems of concern to the pilots, such as: cabin pressurization and atmosphere control; windscreen demisting and wiping; and, in military combat aircraft, avionics which will respond to high levels of G so that the pilot's flying suit is inflated to prevent loss of blood from the brain.

Simulating

Air forces have usually employed special

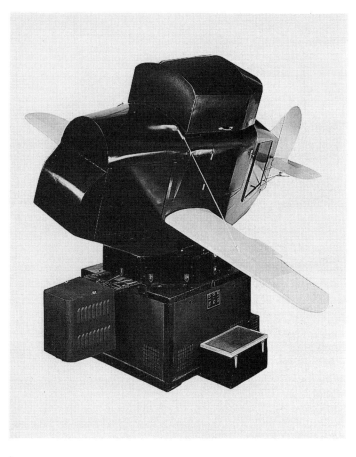

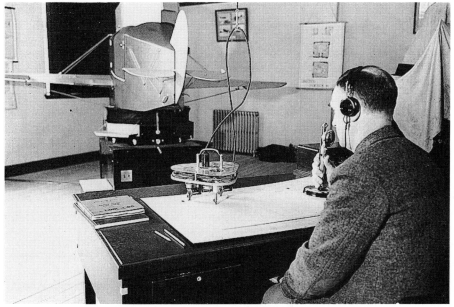

Above *Link trainer,* circa *1946.* (Link Miles)

Left *The Link trainer. The instructor monitored the pupil's progress using the track inked on the chart by the 'crab' which moved in response to the simulator.* (via Aeroplane Monthly)

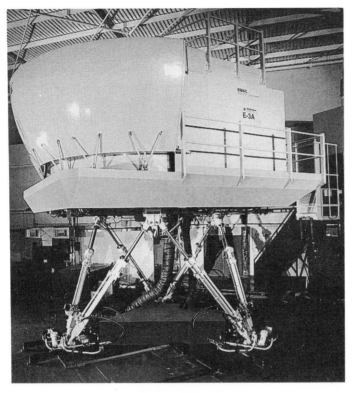

The exterior of a modern simulator, which enables the crew of a Boeing E-3A to complete a sortie without leaving the ground. (Rediffusion Simulation)

'under the hood'. The instructor could even select turbulence to add to the pupil's problems of endeavouring to fly procedural patterns, interceptions of radio range, Lorenz and ILS beams.

Part of its success stemmed from the simple construction which encouraged production, particularly during the Second World War. Essentially it used church organ constructional techniques so that the turning motor, for example, was a bank of bellows operating cranks connected to the shaft on which the trainer rotated. Pitch and roll were effected by large bellows. A 'crab' powered by small electric motors 'crawled' across a chart, in response to positional signals from the cockpit unit, so that the instructor could monitor a pupil's progress during a simulated flight.

Using the Link as a starting point and applying electronics, the simulator was elaborated and its quality of simulation vastly improved. The introduction of digital computers and wide-screen colour television provided a realistic view ahead. Pilots could now train in a simulator which replicated to a high degree a real aircraft and a real world seen through the flight deck windows. Over the years simulators also progressed to incorporate very realistic roll, pitch, bank and heave motions.

Such is the level of realism achieved by modern simulators that the licensing authorities permit their use for the renewal of a pilot's instrument rating certificate.

Combat aircraft pilots can fly a complete sortie in a simulator. This not only replicates all the controls and instruments, as well as communication and weapon systems, its simulation of the external scene can include ground features and targets as well as hostile aircraft. Two pilots can fly their simulators against each other in bloodless combat: each sees the other's 'aircraft' projected on the visual scene.

aircraft types dedicated to the training role: less so with civil operators. But both use simulators of varying degrees of realism.

The use of simulated cockpits has been a time and cost saving training method since the earliest years of flight. Many different ideas have been tried. The majority in the first twenty years were simple mechanical systems used to demonstrate the action of the primary controls and to teach hand, eye and sensory co-ordination. Later came reaction teachers using a system of light patterns to which the pupil had to respond.

The most important improvement in simulators came with the Link trainer (1929). This was an enclosed cockpit equipped with instruments and controls able to simulate roll, pitch and turning. It was a 'sweat box' in which the pupil learnt to maintain control when flying

CHAPTER THIRTEEN

STATE OF THE TECHNOLOGY

Progress

The civil flight deck of the 1980s emphasizes the progress which has been made in aviation. It also provides a starting point or foundation for considering future developments.

In only 87 years aviation has come a long way; speed has increased fivefold; passenger capacity by 500 times; and safety has improved significantly. When Orville Wright lay prone on the lower wing of the first Flyer his immediate concern was with success or failure after years of experimental work. He may even have thought about the future of aviation but it is unlikely that he could have foreseen the extent to which civil aviation would eventually progress.

The modern flight deck exhibits little, if anything, that we can use to relate back to the epic first flight at Kill Devil in December 1903. Perhaps the primary control lever set at each pilot's outboard knee in an A320 evokes a retrospective look at the Wrights' control levers? The large adjustable seats bear no relation to flight much before 1945. The colour CRT displays on which the pilots depend for much of their information only extend as far back in history as Stanley Kubrick's film *2001* of 1968; even the monochrome CRTs of radar only take us back to 1940.

Yet one item of flight deck equipment has changed little over the years: the rudder pedals. These are, after all, only a refined version of the rudder bar used by Bleriot in 1909 when he flew the English Channel: as we have seen, the earliest Wright machines did not have a foot-operated control for the rudder.

Wheel and stick

The shape of the wheel and its supporting pole or arm has exhibited numerous variations in transport aircraft. The majority of these variations have been used for one or more of the following reasons: mechanical convenience; common use by two pilots; improving the pilot's view of the instruments; improving access to the pilot's seat.

Essentially the roll-pitch hand control requires only one or two handles moving along an arc whose centre is on a line extending from the pilot's diaphragm. Historically, the wheel and its later equivalents were there to make the best use of the pilot's muscles and to cope with large aileron and elevator movements.

Among the many variations of the primary aileron-elevator control, that tried in a twin-engine Armagnac in the 1950s was one of the more unusual. With the object of eliminating as far as possible

interference with the pilot's view of the instruments by the control column and wheel — a common problem — the designer looked at the controls of tracked vehicles. Might their twin lever for steering be ideal for an aircraft? Hence each pilot in the Armagnac had two control levers or 'sticks'. Pulled or pushed together they operated the elevators for pitch control: moved differentially up and down they controlled the ailerons for roll control. But nothing more came of this idea.

Power controls eventually did away for the need for muscle power, but the wheel remained. The pilot needed somewhere to put his hands and a mounting had to be found for the autopilot cut-out, microphone and other switches.

The wheel is, conveniently, a two-handed input. But its demise is near. Its successor, the side-stick control, is a complete departure from a tradition which survived for over 75 years. We have

reached a time in the history of aviation analogous to that in the seventeenth century when the large spoked wheel replaced the whipstaff and tiller in a sailing ship. In the Airbus A320, for example, there is just one side-stick 'fighter type' control on the outboard side of each pilot. Using just one hand the pilot can control the aircraft in roll and pitch.

This type of simple, space-saving, primary control was made practicable by 'fly-by-wire' technology.

For over 75 years the majority of aircraft types had the primary control surfaces (rudder, elevator and ailerons) connected directly by mechanical systems to the pilot's hand and foot controls (wheel/column and rudder pedals). Even if there were power-operated controls these did not necessarily break the continuity of direct connection between the pilot and the controlling surfaces. Given all the variations and combinations of hydraulics and electrics, if all else failed, the pilot's muscles could provide 'last resort' control effort.

Fly-by-wire, as a revolutionary concept in which there are no mechanical links between the pilot and the control surfaces, has obviated the need for large-movement, muscle-assisting, hand controls; particularly for aileron and elevator operation. Because control in a fly-by-wire system (FBW) is effected by digital electronic signals then only a small lever, such as the side-stick control in the Airbus 320, is needed.

An important design requirement with FBW is the need to give the pilot 'feel' or 'feedback'. In a direct mechanical control system the pilot can feel the control loads being applied to the aircraft and can also feel its response. In many power-assisted systems artificial loads are added to the pilot's controls to prevent the aircraft from being overstressed. Similarly the small 'one-hand' aileron-elevator side-stick of FBW can be arranged to offer resistance to excessive input movements on the part of the pilot; although in the Airbus 320, for example, and also in some fighter aircraft with FBW, the pilot can apply maximum bank and pitch (aileron and elevator) without feeling any resistance to the movement of the control column or side-stick. However, the aircraft is protected from excessive control demands, which could result in structural failure or a stall, by the FBW system's computer, which is programmed to limit excessive control demands.

The side stick control and the all-

The flight deck of a Lockheed TriStar. The forward windows afford the pilots wide arcs-of-view. The control yokes were not chosen just because of their interesting shape but because they did not obstruct the pilots' view of the instruments. (Smiths Industries)

The flight deck of an A300 Airbus used for evaluating the side-stick controller. An extended seat arm rest provides support for steady movement of the pilot's hand. The side stick saves weight, improves the view of the instruments and simplifies maintenance. (Airbus Industrie)

electronic displays in the Airbus have certainly brought a significant change to the civil flight deck as far as the pilot is concerned.

The removal of the primary aileron-elevator manual control wheel or spectacle and its replacement by a side stick has given the two pilots a control position which is more like the desk of a computer operator. The Airbus is an illustration of control being exercised for the greater part of flight by the pilots through the equivalent of a computer terminal.

In aircraft with conventional wheel control in front of each pilot the two sets of primary controls are mechanically linked together. In the unlikely event of a disagreement between the pilots as to which way to turn or push or pull, the stronger wins. But the side-stick, fly-by-wire, controls of the A320 are not linked by any mechanical connections.

The flight manual for the Airbus 320 neatly answers any questions about 'who wins' by the simple statement, 'The intelligent pilot wins, not the strongest'. This statement is easier to accept when we remember that the flight control systems automatically ignore any control inputs such as an excessive bank angle demand by the pilot or inputs which will induce a stall or 'pull the wings off '.

However, one pilot can 'override' the other by pressing the button on the control stick. Interestingly the FBW control in the Airbus 320 is 'backed up' by mechanical 'direct link' elevator and rudder controls. So that in the remote event that all the parallel and independent channels of the FBW fail, the pilots can retain elevator and rudder control. The flight control computers also take over the application of up elevator during a turn.

In aircraft equipped with a control wheel for roll control the wheel can be moved through an arc of about 80 degrees. With the side-sticks of the Airbus 320 FBW system the pilot's wrist movement is limited to only 20 degrees of arc.

Colour on the flight deck

The CRT colour displays used for primary flight display of aircraft speed, vertical speed, heading, altitude and attitude as well as navigational information have introduced one of the major departures from the Basic T layout of the discrete electro-mechanical instruments. When CRT displays were first introduced, designers, and for that matter, pilots, clung to the then traditional layout in which the primary aircraft attitude

display, such as an attitude director, had to be above the navigational display, such as the horizontal situation indicator. Therefore the primary displays in front of each pilot were placed vertically. In the Airbus and other transport aircraft with similar electronic instrumentation, the two primary displays are placed side by side.

Larger colour CRTs became available in the late 1980s and they considerably improved the pilot's place. Large, eight-inch for example, CRTs improve both the efficiency and appearance of the flight deck of a transport aircraft.

When colour CRT displays were introduced as part of an electronic instrumentation system (EIS) their technology was revolutionary. However, the display formats, i.e. the arrangement of the symbols and alphanumerics, was conventional. They tended to replicate

The cockpit of the General Dynamics F 16 fighter. A side-stick control is used which improves the overall ergonomics of the cockpit. The sides of the ejection seat can be seen extending toward the pilot's knees. Because the HUD can provide the majority of instrumental information, the conventional instruments are few in number compared with cockpits of an earlier generation. (via Aeroplane Monthly)

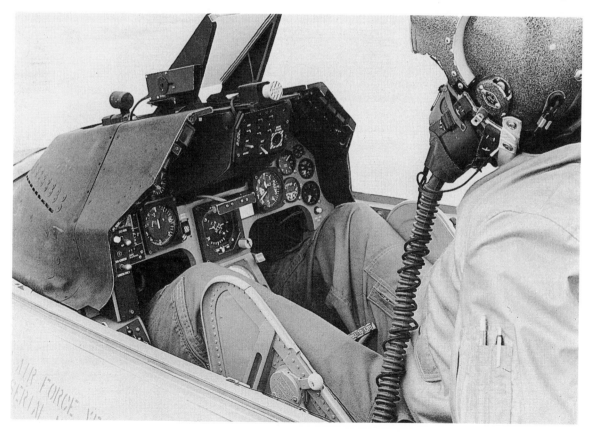

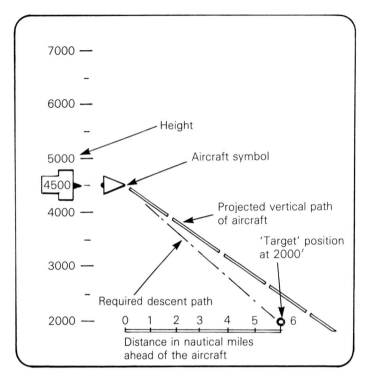

7000 —

-

6000 —

-

Height

5000 —

Aircraft symbol

4500

4000 —

Projected vertical path
of aircraft

'Target' position
at 2000'

3000 —

-

Required descent path

2000 —   0   1   2   3   4   5   6

Distance in nautical miles
ahead of the aircraft

*Vertical situation
display (VSD). The
typical format has
been simplified to
show an aircraft at
4,500 feet and
descending. The
projected path line
indicates that the rate
of descent must be
increased to achieve
the 2,000 feet
position.* (Author)

the formats of the electro-mechanical attitude director and horizontal situation indicator. With experience, new formats were evolved; particularly for the attitude display, which then combined attitude information with speed, vertical speed and altitude.

The flexibility afforded by the operative ease with which computer software can be changed has enabled the designers of these displays to make a contiguous series of detail changes intended to 'fine tune' the ergonomics.

When the ergonomists studied the flight deck displays needed for the Boeing 7J7 they considered a number of concepts. One, which had been evaluated by NASA in the 1970s, provided the pilot with three CRTs: one for the 'vertical', one for the horizontal or map view, and the third for a 'side view'. This combination of displays would give a 3D 'picture' of the aircraft in relation to the horizon, the navigational aids (such as an instrument approach localizer beam) and to the

approach path seen from one side.

Using the 'side view' display the pilot will 'see' his aircraft as if he were standing to one side of its flight path. The symbol of the aircraft is close to the top left-hand corner of the screen. The computer-generated information on the approach profile is caused to flow to the left so as to give an apparent motion of the aircraft from left to right.

A number of formats have been studied for the future use of the 'side view' display. For example, the computer could generate an ideal approach path as a profile line, so that the pilot can monitor the progress of the flight. At the same time, another line shows the projected path of the aircraft.

This is, of course, just one of many possible display techniques. The electronic and computer specialists can virtually give the pilot any combination of colour, symbols and alphanumerics. Their relative usefulness will only be shown by in-service experience.

Together the fly-by-wire side stick control and the electronic displays along with their associated computer based systems have revolutionized the flight deck and the work of the pilot in a way which was hardly envisaged in the 1960s. But what they have not done is to change the responsibility and ultimate authority of the pilot.

Digital Airbus

The Airbus 320 is a good example of how modern digital computer and digital data bus technology revolutionized the design and use of the flight deck in the 1980s.

An A320 crew becomes involved with and dependent on computers and electronic displays from the moment they enter the flight operations office. All the information needed for the pre-flight briefing is stored on computer memories. Their data can be displayed on screens for study by the crew.

Much of the flight information, which includes specified air traffic control routes, has already been loaded into the onboard computers of the aircraft's flight management system.

The external visual check of the aircraft is still carried out by a member of the crew but the all-important electronics can only be checked by the system's own self-checking circuits. The CRT displays on the flight deck show, system by system, the health of each. The navigation pages of the computer memory are called up on the screen so that the captain and first officer have all the data needed to fly the aircraft off the ground and on into the selected departure pattern of headings and heights requested by air traffic control.

The flight management computer has been checked so that it knows the loading gate number at the departure airfield. Once the aircraft starts to taxi, the system's computer stores in its memory every turn and distance moved, so that it knows with considerable accuracy at what point on the ground or in the air the aircraft has reached. Throughout the flight and without the intervention of the crew, the flight management system re-

checks its positional data by referring to each of the radio navigational aids, such as VORs and DMEs, which are within range at any one time. The system is also controlling the aircraft's speed, heading, vertical speed and attitude by commanding both the automatic flight control system and the thrust control unit of each engine. This ensures that the aircraft is flown not only in accordance with the desired route, but that it keeps to the most efficient vertical profile.

The main features of the A320 flight deck are undoubtedly the side-stick primary flight controls for roll and pitch and the 'wall-to-wall' array of six colour CRTs; eight if we include the CRT displays of the flight management system (FMS) units on the central pedestal.

The side-sticks give an uninterrupted view of the main instrument panel. The six main CRT displays provide all the information needed to control the aircraft or monitor its automatic performance throughout all the different operating modes.

As with most CRT electronic instrument systems (EIS), the six displays in the

Arcs-of-view when seated in the Captain's (left-hand) seat of an Airbus A320. (Author)

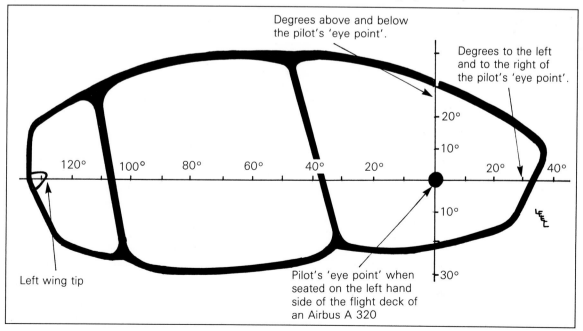

Degrees above and below the pilot's 'eye point'.

Degrees to the left and to the right of the pilot's 'eye point'.

20°
10°

120°   100°   80°   60°   40°   20°   20°   40°

10°

Left wing tip

Pilot's 'eye point' when seated on the left hand side of the flight deck of an Airbus A 320

30°

The 'digital' flight deck — Airbus A320. The side-stick controllers have made room for an improved instrument and controls layout and pull out desk for each pilot. There are eight CRT colour display units, six on the main panel and the two flight management system control units on the central pedestal. This is a modern flight deck designed to enable the pilots to act as managers of the aircraft. (Airbus Industrie)

A320 can be selected by the pilots to show a particular set of information. For example, normally the outboard unit of the two CRTs in front of each pilot is used as the primary flight display (PFD). This presents colour graphics, symbols and alphanumerics of: attitude, airspeed (knots) and Mach number, altitude and vertical speed, heading, automatic flight system status, ILS and radio altitude. With origins stretching back to the Basic Six of the 1930s, the PFD format is based on the Basic T.

The inboard unit of the two CRTs in front of each pilot is used as the navigation display (ND), i.e. the horizontal or 'map' situation.

The other two CRTs, on the centre panel, normally show electronic centralized aircraft monitor (ECAM) information. The upper for engine performance and status and the lower for aircraft systems; such as hydraulics, electrics and fuel. However, in the event of a failure in one display unit, the PFD for example, the information can be switched to another screen.

Until the advent of all-electronic displays and their associated computers each instrument was isolated. If one failed, the crew had to rely on the remaining instruments. If both attitude directors were to fail, the pilots had to use a standby attitude indicator.

Despite the all-electronic display philosophy for the A320 flight deck and also for other aircraft, standby electromechanical or barometric airspeed, altitude and attitude instruments are still provided — just in case! Which suggests that 'clockwork' instruments will continue to be found on the flight decks of aircraft flying in the twenty-first century.

During the design of the A320 flight deck, decisions had to be reached about the relative importance and relative positions of each item. For the overhead panel, on which are mounted circuit breakers, engine fire controls, hydraulic, fuel and electrical selectors as well as air conditioning, the auxiliary power unit panel and others, the design philosophy used was one of 'lights out'. In other words, unless the crew needed to know about the status or condition of a particular system there would be no indication.

For the greater part of a flight the management of the aircraft is monitored through the electronic centralized aircraft monitor (ECAM). Similar systems are used in other modern aircraft; EICAS for example (engine indication and crew alert system). All use colour electronic displays and touch or keypad interfaces through which the crew inserts or requests information.

The use of colour displays on the flight deck, such as CRTs or a matrix of LEDs (light emitting diodes) and LCDs (liquid crystal displays), which differentiate between various operating functions and states, helps the crew to assimilate information quickly.

The flight deck of the A320 brings into focus the role of the civil pilot of the 1980s. In the past twenty years the function of the pilot has become more concerned with managing a flight. The pilot is no longer required to exercise continuous and detailed 'hands on' control of the aircraft. This task is now the province of the computer-based systems, which when given a specific set of instructions or tasks carry them out. The pilot's task is to monitor the systems and be able at all times to adapt and improvise whenever a rare situation or set of circumstances arise. This is where the pilot's own massive computer, the human brain, comes into its own.

As an example of the relationship between the skills and responsibilities of pilot and computer there is the situation where the aircraft suffers a major technical fault, such as engine failure. Once the crew has dealt with the immediate problem of the failed engine, the flight management system can be asked to display the options available. These might include the nearest airfield matched to the aircraft's landing weight

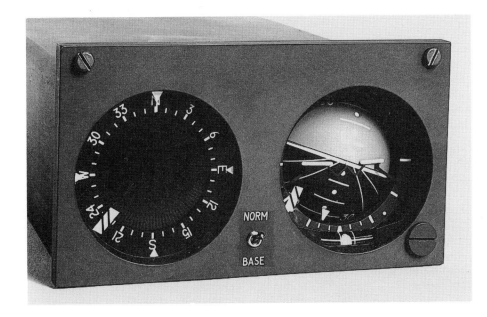

Stand-by heading and attitude instruments for the EAP fighter.
(Smiths Industries)

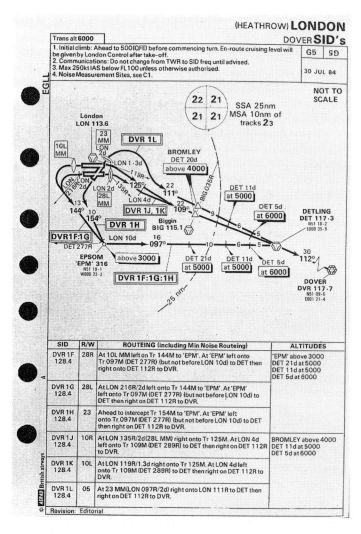

SID	R/W	ROUTEING (including Min Noise Routeing)	ALTITUDES
DVR 1F 128.4	28R	At 10L MM left on Tr 144M to 'EPM'. At 'EPM' left onto Tr 097M (DET 277R) (but not before LON 10d) to DET then right onto DET 112R to DVR.	'EPM' above 3000 / DET 21d at 5000 / DET 11d at 5000 / DET 5d at 6000
DVR 1G 128.4	28L	At LON 216R/2d left onto Tr 144M to 'EPM'. At 'EPM' left onto Tr 097M (DET 277R) (but not before LON 10d) to DET then right onto DET 112R to DVR.	
DVR 1H 128.4	23	Ahead to intercept Tr 154M to 'EPM'. At 'EPM' left onto Tr 097M (DET 277R) (but not before LON 10d) to DET then right onto DET 112R to DVR.	
DVR 1J 128.4	10R	At LON 135R/2d(28L MM) right onto Tr 125M. At LON 4d left onto Tr 109M (DET 289R) to DET then right onto DET 112R to DVR.	BROMLEY above 4000 / DET 11d at 5000 / DET 5d at 6000
DVR 1K 128.4	10L	At LON 119R/1.3d right onto Tr 125M. At LON 4d left onto Tr 109M (DET 289R) to DET then right onto DET 112R to DVR.	
DVR 1L 128.4	05	At 23 MM(LON 097R/2d) right onto LON 111R to DET then right on DET 112R to DVR.	

Standard Instrument Departure 'plate'. This emphasizes the extent to which the crew of an aircraft have to conform to specific headings, altitudes and speed datums when flying within a control zone. (AERAD/British Airways)

and required landing run as well as its relationship to the visibility conditions. It might come up with two or three airfields, each of which has a number of advantages and disadvantages. This is where the human brain has the advantage at present because it can assimilate many different courses of action and detailed circumstances — such as the remote possibility of a passenger at the same time becoming seriously ill and requiring urgent medical attention; something which it is not practicable to programme into a computer.

An important feature of civil aviation is the degree of control exercised by the air traffic control (ATC) systems. Long gone are the days when the pilot in command of an airliner took the most direct route available to the destination. With the growth in air traffic came the need for separation to avoid collision, and regulation to avoid congestion around and on airports. Increasingly, civil aircraft were being confined to ATC defined routes, specified reporting points, and being allocated heights at which to fly.

The increase in air traffic control has, in some ways, compromised the authority of the pilot in command. Except in an emergency a captain does not depart from the headings and flight levels required by the ATC controllers. Even speed has to be kept within certain limits when flying in a terminal control area.

It has been suggested that because the headings, speeds and heights flown are to meet the requirements of ATC then the ATC computers should control aircraft directly. Then what of the pilot's authority and responsibility?

The fighter/attack aircraft

The military pilot in a combat aircraft obviously works in a very different operating environment from that of the transport aircraft pilot. The solo military pilot requires as many aids, if not more, as the civil pilot.

The fighter/attack aircraft operating scenario includes periods of flight when the speed of events is very much greater than that experienced by the civil pilot. In addition to flying the aircraft from base to an operational position, such as a ground target or tactical patrol position at high altitude, the pilot has to manage a complex weapon system. Complex because it is often made up of a number of different elements, such as missiles, bombs, electronic countermeasures (ECM) and electronic target acquisition, used in different operating modes.

Selection of a particular weapon, such as air-to-air missiles, requires instant judgement on the part of the pilot. Unlike the airline pilot he cannot consult with other crew members. He is on his own. He has at all times to exercise extreme vigilance, using his eyes and ears to detect any activity on the part of the enemy. Although, in its essentials, this set of circumstances is similar to that in a fighter/attack cockpit of 1918 or 1940 there are two additional and very significant elements. These are the speed with which the tactical situation can change and the cost of the aircraft.

The most effective use has to be made of such an expensive weapon system. This includes navigating to, identifying and attacking a target irrespective of night or poor visibility, undulating terrain, hostile radars and ground-to-air missiles and flying as low as possible to delay detection. This cannot be done with a 'simple' aircraft equipped with 'simple' systems and consequently few instruments and controls. For these reasons alone the modern combat cockpit is an 'expensive' place.

The cost is reflected in the number of controls and instruments in the cockpit. The wide range of instruments, electronic displays, buttons, switches, levers and illuminated panels, as well as warning annunciators, are there to enable the human pilot to make the most effective use of a machine whose first cost is measured in tens of millions of pounds. There is also the cost of training the pilot, which may be another million or more. The 200 or so hours to train a Hurricane pilot in 1940 cost much less and his aircraft less than £50,000 at today's value.

At one time, the fighter pilot was always 'on top of the job'. His physical and mental abilities and their limitations were at a level far above the aerodynamic, structural and performance limits of the aircraft. But in the second half of the twentieth century aircraft speed and manoeuvrability steadily overtook the mental and physical limits of the pilot. In other words, pilots have been increasingly subjected to higher and higher levels of G and to ever increasing amounts of information. At the same time, the speeds at which fighter/attack

Pilot's view of the HUD symbols superimposed on the real world ahead of the aircraft. (GEC Avionics/Major C. Killberg USAF)

aircraft operate against each other have compressed an engagement to less than 30 seconds. By the 1980s a pilot was having to manoeuvre into a tactically advantageous position, 'kill' the enemy and get back onto an 'escape' course to base, all within 20 or 30 seconds.

In this short time the pilot has to operate close to the limits of this mental abilities, while he is being subjected to high levels of G. Of course, G leads to G-LOC: G induced loss of consciousness. If the pilot is forced to 'pull' excessive G for more than a few seconds, in order to keep the advantage in a dogfight, he may black out until the G forces reduce. However, the effects last for much longer and the pilot may not be immediately aware of what is happening even though his sight has returned. He will not be aware that his skills have been degraded to an extent that he loses control of the aircraft or falls victim to his opponent who has a higher level of tolerance to G.

In the 1980s it was increasingly realized that the situational awareness of the pilot, particularly in military aircraft, had to be improved. Situational awareness is jargon for the ability to be aware at all times of what is happening to the aircraft's trajectory and of the operating environment. The latter includes information about hostile missiles, aircraft, radars and of all the visual and electronic inputs needed by the pilot for making split-second decisions. To improve the pilot's decision making and to reduce workload, three-dimensional (3D) displays have been developed so that their information, in the form of symbols and graphics, matches as closely as possible the real world outside the cockpit.

These advanced displays will not only reduce pilot workload but also enable the pilot to cope with an always increasing number of electronic warfare systems. In the late 1980s the concept emerged of the 'Big Picture'. Essentially this eliminated the demarcation which existed for over 80 years between the outside view of the real world and the 'inside' view of the instruments. Big Picture is a large format display of computer generated symbols, analogues of the real world and a view of the real world derived from direct vision by the pilot or via low-light TV and forward-looking infra red (FLIR). All this information is merged on the one big screen in front of the pilot.

On the Big Picture can be seen all the information normally gained from individual electronic displays — such as primary flight data, weapon and system status. Information obtained by the aircraft's sensors is also displayed so that the pilot can actually see the position of threats, such as radar or approaching missiles. It also displays the various targets in such a way that the pilot is able to see which of his electronic sensors has made the detection.

Big Picture is even more versatile: it also acts as a control interface between pilot and aircraft. Using a combination of voice control and touching a specific part of the display, the pilot can indicate a target. Touching and speaking will, for example, interrogate one of the aircraft systems.

Part of the Big Picture technique is the

Far left *A Tornado front cockpit showing the extensive range of controls and instruments needed to make the most effective use of a very expensive multi-role combat aircraft.* (British Aerospace)

Below *Multi-purpose colour display for an advanced fighter, combining raster (as in a domestic TV) with cursive (ie stroke-written) symbols and alphanumerics. The map mode is shown with a 16 nm circle centred on the present position of the aircraft. The vertical line indicates the aircraft's heading which is passing just to the right of the small circle marked 26, which is the next waypoint 20 nm ahead.* (Ferranti)

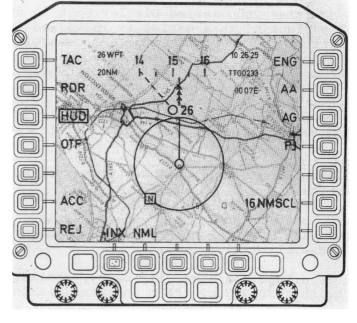

'Big Picture' — one large electronic display screen. The pilot uses touch, voice and helmet pointing to indicate, select, command and initiate modes, functions and actions.

1. *On the upper area of the screen the pilot sees head-up display (HUD) and weapon-aiming symbols and alphanumerics superposed on the view of the real world. At night or in poor visibility low light television or infra red views are used.*
2. *Television or infra red sensors produce a view below the nose of the aircraft.*
3. *The sides of the display are used to present systems information such as fuel, engine, communications and weapon 'stores'.*
4. *HUD symbols and alphanumerics.*
5. *Pilot's visor used for pointing.*

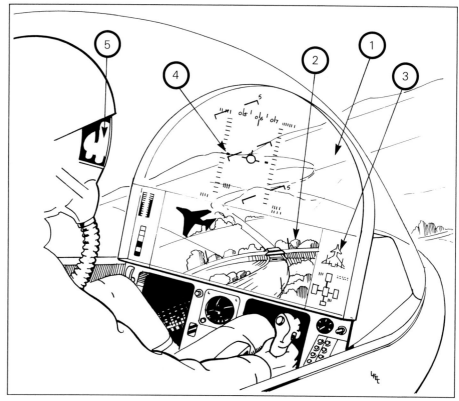

presentation of information so as to appear three-dimensional. Another attribute is the opportunity it affords the pilot of selecting a different 'point of view'. For example the computer-generated view of the world can be seen as if from a position behind the aircraft. As with some video computer games, the pilot can fly his aircraft against the 'background' of sky and ground. The pilot might even take a position to one side of his aircraft. There is an alternative to Big Picture. This is the projection of information on the pilot's visor.

New technologies and the future

As technology has advanced, successive generations of pilots have had to adapt to the new and sometimes strange. Today we have fully automatic, hands-off, flight without reference to the real world. Prior

to the 1930s such an idea was viewed with some concern by some pilots because the overall technology of aviation within their experience was limited. Today the most recent generation of pilots and those about to take up flying live in a vastly different world: a world in which they have come to accept the abilities and reliability of the computer. Therefore they do not expect to have controls directly connected to the aircraft control surface and neither do they expect that instrument displays will be limited to analogue presentations; such as a pointer moving over a circular scale.

New generations of pilots grow up in a world in which electronic displays and simplified control inputs dominate. In the classroom they are introduced to the computer terminals at an early age and much of the domestic equipment around them has electronic displays of some form or other. Earlier generations of pilots had become accustomed to wheels, levers and knobs as accepted methods of controlling machines and vehicles.

From the earliest days of automatic and semi-automatic control systems, designers and pilots have debated the extent to which, in a particular flight mode, the pilot becomes part of the control loop. Keeping the pilot in the loop is, essentially, a matter of sufficient information input on what is happening and, importantly, what will happen.

Increasingly, in both military and civil aircraft, the pilot is becoming part of an 'outer' control loop. In other words the pilot exercises the undoubted human skill, compared with the computer, of decision making among a number of complex inter-relationships from which options can be derived. But this particular human ability will be limited to that outer loop of control and will involve, as it does today, monitoring progress and selecting waypoints and flight modes. The actual control of the many interdependent aircraft systems will be the province of the computer. This 'work sharing' might be described as 'coarse' control by the pilot and 'fine' control by the computer. In a 'fly-by-wire' (no mechanical reversion) aircraft the pilot cannot intervene in the inner loop.

Three lines of research and development which will have a significant influence on the design of cockpits and flight decks for the year 2000 and beyond are: direct voice input (DVI), symbionics and the 'pilot associate' concept, and thought control. Although the latter may be much further off than the other two.

Direct voice input (DVI) has been developed to an effective level and in the late 1980s was in use in some military aircraft. It is used to improve the man-machine interface including reducing pilot workload. As it implies, DVI uses a speech-recognition computer which interprets commands and questions spoken by the pilot. It initiates the appropriate commands and selection processes of other systems, for example: 'Emergency radio' — two spoken words instead of a number of key selections on control panels.

DVI is not just, therefore, an elegant way of commanding and interrogating an aircraft without the need to use the fingers as selectors and controllers. DVI helps to avoid a high workload interface in which the pilot has to concentrate on exacting, precise, ordered key-pressing sequences so as to initiate specific commands or to interrogate the different systems.

Interactive, real-time, continuous voice recognition is now an accepted technique for improving the control interface. Direct voice input (DVI) has not been pursued just for the sake of advancing the overall technology. It is, perhaps, one of those examples of necessity boosting a specific technological advance.

Of course, to use DVI effectively a pilot has to control his speech both in quality and content. This can be achieved in the comparative 'calm' of the transport aircraft flight deck; but during combat the cockpit of a fighter, in which the pilot sustains high G loads and his breathing is affected by life support gases supplied under pressure and anti-G pressure garments, is a hostile environment for DVI.

Symbionics is a word derived from symbiosis, biology and electronics. It is likely to be the key element in the overall ergonomics of the future. It is both an alternative and inter-active element: a computer whose user-friendly faculties enable it to prompt, advise and warn the pilot. In practice it is likely to develop not as a discrete system but as one of the primary functions of the principal aircraft computer.

A symbionic computer forming part of the control interface will be the 'conscience' of the pilot. It will be programmed to 'think' as far as possible in the way in which the pilot thinks. The total symbionic system will consist of both the human pilot and the computer. This composite will combine the best attributes of both elements in the most effective way. When — not if — this concept is realized, knowledge-based, or artificial intelligence, computers will have become a common feature. The symbionic computer will be the Dr Jekyll to Mr Hyde the pilot.

Current interfaces are usually user-friendly: that is they provide unambiguous information; they offer menus covering different operating modes; and they both prompt the user and respond to a cry for 'help'. The symbionic aircraft system will be more than user-friendly, it will be a confidante and guide.

Symbionics, such as a 'pilot associate', can convey high level concepts to the pilot via the control interface. These can be communicated to the pilot via electronic displays, synthesized speech, music and other non-verbal sounds or even smells. Unfortunately the communication of complex information in the other direction, i.e. from pilot to the system, has yet to be perfected. For some time to come the pilot's input 'vocabulary' is likely to be limited to discrete key and touch inputs, eye and head pointing and to simple, formalized DVI inputs.

Thought control is one of the more advanced areas of research which has been 'thought' about for a number of years. Specific electrical signals from the human brain have been identified and which correspond to different emotional states. Thought control will revolutionize the cockpit and flight deck. It may lie somewhere in the future, but it will happen.

A line of research which is undoubtedly already within the grasp of modern technologies is the 'blank' cockpit. In place of electronic displays and other types of indicator, all visual data and information will be projected, focused at infinity, onto the pilot's view of the real world outside the aircraft. This technique, using helmet-mounted sights, has already been developed for specialized tasks, such as target marking in helicopters.

If these ideas, as well as thought control, are successfully developed to their limits, then the fighter cockpit, and even the flight deck, will be significantly different in the future. Perhaps, within two generations of military aircraft from now, the pilot will be totally enclosed, with no direct view of the real world. The pilot's helmet will provide communication, by voice and thought, and a synthesized view of the real world which will be combined, as with present-day HUDs, with symbols and graphical information projected onto the pilot's eyes.

However, before progress along these lines can be achieved there has to be a big reduction in the weight of all helmet-mounted equipment. Otherwise the pilot will be subjected to unacceptable neck loads during high-G combat and when ejecting.

Summary

The following is a summary of some of the key factors in the evolution of the pilot's place over the past 87 years.

Early on in the evolution of the cockpit the principle was established of hands for roll and pitch control and feet for yaw control. For three decades the pilot was expected to effect control of a basically unstable vehicle, the aircraft, using the perceived sensations of movement and without the assistance of instruments. With the need to continue flight in cloud, at night, and in poor visibility, without losing control, 'blind' flying instruments came into regular use in the 1930s.

Once aviation became a reliable form of transport, flights were attempted over oceans and featureless terrain. Such flights required navigational instruments.

Communication between an aircraft and the ground, over long distances and irrespective of the visibility, encouraged the development of aircraft radio: first for communication and later for navigation. These functions increased the amount of equipment in the pilot's place.

The introduction of more complex

aircraft engines, whose efficient operation depended on frequent and detailed attention on the part of the pilot, encouraged the development of engine instruments. And so another set of instruments was added to the cockpit.

In the early decades of aviation, and in light and sporting aircraft to this day, the pilot usually had wide arcs of vision, particularly from an open cockpit. But as aircraft became larger or more powerful, instruments proliferated and the pilot found that the view ahead had to be shared with the instrument panels.

Until about 1935 there were few serious attempts to apply logic to the arrangement of the instruments. The practice, particularly in American aircraft with fixed-pitch propellers when flying 'blind', of concentrating on the turn and slip, airspeed and RPM indicators encouraged placing them in a group on the panel

The introduction of the gyro-stabilized artificial horizon and the gyro heading indicator, in the early 1930s, resulted in new instrument panel arrangements. More thought was being given to the man-machine interface. In Britain the RAF, which had to fly irrespective of the visibility conditions, specified the Basic Six Panel. In 1937 this became the standard for new aircraft.

The development of 'command' type instruments, such as the Sperry zero reader, in place of instruments which only told you what had happened and not what to do to correct errors, formed a milestone in cockpit evolution. The 'command' type instruments were designed to give the pilot clear and unambiguous information about what had to be done in order to achieve a specific flight path or manoeuvre.

In about 1965 electronic, solid-state, instruments began to take over from some of the electro-mechanical types. By 1975 the number of electronic displays was increasing every year. In the 1980s new aircraft were being equipped with electronic instrumentation systems (EIS)

and the older types of instruments were relegated to a 'stand-by' function.

Inertial navigation systems of the 1960s not only improved the accuracy of track-keeping over oceans and away from radio beacons, such as VORs, they simplified the navigational tasks. This in turn affected the design of the flight deck and the forward part of transport aircraft — particularly when there was no need to provide a navigator's station.

The electro-mechanical horizontal situation (HS) indicator of the 1960s was an important step in improving the display of 'map' information. But the electronic instrument systems (EIS) with their colour CRT displays of 'map' information were a far more important step. On one display the pilot was given all the navigational facts and relationships, both in time and distance. The EIS combined the one-time navigator's chart, the inertial navigation displays, the RMIs (radio magnetic indicator) and a mass of other information in such a way that it could be quickly interpreted. There was no need to transfer the information to other instruments. The pilot no longer had to make mental calculations when checking the position of the aircraft or when determining where it would be at some future time.

By the time this book is being read no doubt the vertical situation, 'side-view', display will have arrived as a practical addition to the electronic attitude director and horizontal situation displays: it may even be combined with the latter.

Vectored thrust, as used in the Harrier series of VSTOL fighters, introduced an additional primary control into the cockpit. This is the lever, alongside the traditional throttle lever, for selecting the position of the four thrust nozzles over a range of angles between the horizontal 'normal' flight position and the vertical thrust position.

The advent of aircraft whose wings could be positioned in flight at different angles of sweep provided the pilot with yet another important control lever:

wingsweep selection. Variable angle of wingsweep adapts the aircraft's aerodynamic characteristics to height and speed: moderate or no sweep for take-off and landing; maximum sweep for high speed. Important examples are the Panavia Tornado, the F–111 and the F–14. Later versions of the Tornado have automatic wingsweep control, thereby helping to keep down pilot workload.

Which way should the wingsweep control lever move? Back to increase sweep or forward for high speed in the same direction as throttle movement for more thrust? Basic ergonomics recommend that a control should move in the same sense or direction as the controlled system or equipment. Therefore a wingsweep control lever should move back for increased sweep. Yet the other way has been used. For when General Dynamics came to design the cockpit and its equipment for the F–111 it was decided that the pilot's sweep control lever should move forward, the logic adopted being that for high speed the throttles are pushed forward, therefore the sweep lever should move in the same direction for the high-speed fully-swept position of the wings.

Two recent control modes for fighter aircraft have added a new dimension to flight and provided the pilot with additional primary controls. These are direct lift control (DLC) and direct side force control (DSFC). With DLC the pilot can cause the aircraft to ascend and descend without having to raise or lower the nose. DSFC enables the pilot to move the aircraft sideways and at the same time keep the nose pointed in the original direction. If, for example, a pilot attacking a ground target finds that the aircraft, and therefore its weapons, are not pointing at the target then instead of having to roll or alter pitch to correct his aim, DLC and DSFC can be used to quickly alter the flight path. The aircraft can be moved bodily up and down as well as sideways.

Direct lift control is not confined to combat aircraft. The Lockheed TriStar,

for example, has DLC as a standard feature. This enables the aircraft to rise and fall relative to the glidepath without having to raise or lower the nose.

The electronic instruments, using CRTs, LEDs or LCDs, contributed significantly to the improvement of the cockpit in the 1980s. They will continue as the primary visual information interface. However, much needs to be done to improve their ergonomics in order to reduce and rationalize the plethora of symbols, graphics and alphanumerics.

The same requirement applies to the input keys of flight management and performance computer systems. The 1980 systems require too many key strokes to be made by the pilot.

Furthermore, electro-mechanical, and even solid-state stand-by, 'get-you-home' instruments need to be re-thought; for in general the information they provide is far less comprehensive than that of the electronic primary displays for which they act as alternatives in the event of a failure.

The fully automatic systems which have been described have undoubtedly improved the relationship between aircraft and pilot. They have enabled a pilot to achieve precise and economical flight paths without excessive workload. Nevertheless it has to be recognized that should an automatic system fail or deteriorate it may result in a disconcerting aircraft performance. And because these systems operate on intangible concepts and digital bits and logic, the pilot is not always able to make a quick assessment of the best way of intervening in the control loop.

Another part of the flight deck and cockpit which needed improvement in the 1980s was the management of radio and data communication systems. The many different channels provided in modern aircraft and the need to select them in order to match ATC or, for military aircraft, the tactical control requirements increased the pilot's workload. Fortunately by the end of the 1980s this need had been foreseen and communications management systems were being introduced into military aircraft

In the 1980s yet another information display was introduced. This was the control and display panel for the health and usage monitoring system (HUMS). This kept the pilot informed about the 'health' of the principal systems, such as engines. It also kept a check on the rate at which a system's life was being used up.

And finally for this summary are the artificial, knowledge-based, symbionic computer systems which provide an additional 'pilot' in the cockpit or on the flight deck. These 'associate' pilots can warn, caution, advise and retrieve information from an aircraft's data base within a few microseconds. At the same time, they will not suffer from fatigue, fear, age or indecisiveness. Their performance will always be predictable and unaffected by the passage of time.

Yet the human pilot's brain is still one of the most versatile and adaptable computers so far developed. Although unable to match the unflagging ability of the digital computer when it comes to mathematics involving complex masses of numbers, it is able to 'visualize' complicated situations and make quick,

overall, 'broadbrush' judgements.

However remarkable the abilities of computers, they nevertheless have their limitations as 'associate' pilots. Imagine the following perfectly feasible scenario: An aircraft is on the final approach to a landing in daylight. The crew becomes visually aware that another aircraft is making a landing on another runway which intersects theirs. They can see that the other aircraft's undercarriage is down and that the flaps are in the landing position. There is no indication from the airfield control tower that anyone else is aware of the impending danger. The crew, from their experience of the type of aircraft and of their own, realize that a collision will occur unless they initiate a 'go around'.

It can therefore be said that the pilot's place — the aircraft cockpit — in civil aircraft at least is likely to remain that of the human pilot for some time to come. And the definition of that place, as there to protect the pilot, to provide him with a view of the earth and sky, and to house the equipment needed to effect control and navigation, is also likely to remain as applicable to the aircraft of 1903 as those of 1990 and of the future.

GLOSSARY

Glossary of terms, definitions and acronyms primarily related to American and British aviation

A&AEE: Aeroplane & Armament Experimental Establishment of the UK: concerned with testing the suitability of aircraft intended for the Royal Air Force, Royal Navy and the Army Air Corps.

Aileron: a movable control surface on the trailing edge of a wing used to effect roll.

Airspeed Indicator (ASI): one of the primary flight instruments.

ATC: Air Traffic Control: all agencies, systems and control centres responsible for the safe separation of aircraft and for the efficient use of airways.

Aldis sight: a collimated, i.e. focused at infinity, sight used for aiming fixed guns: superseded by the reflector sight.

Alphanumerics: information displayed in the form of numerals and alphabetical characters.

Altimeter: height indicator: one of the primary flight instruments.

Analogue: in instrument presentation the use of pointers or indices moving over graduated circles or lines.

Angle of Attack: the angle between the wing and the relative air flow.

Approach Lights: a pattern of lights formed by a centre line and a series of cross bars of lights which provides visual guidance during a landing.

Attitude: the angle between the aircraft's fore and aft axis line and the horizontal and the angle between the wings and the horizon.

Attitude Director Indicator (ADI): a command type instrument whose indications, when followed by the pilot, enable a selected flight path to be achieved.

Autopilot: a system used to control an aircraft automatically in one or more of the three axis of roll, pitch and yaw.

Automatic Flight Control System (AFCS): a system which controls an aircraft in all three axis and also controls height, speed and vertical speed.

Automatic landing: an extension of the functions of an AFCS using ground-based radio aids and radar altimeters which controls an aircraft throughout landing approach and touchdown.

AVIONICS: aviation electronics.

Basic Six: an arrangement of flight instruments adopted by the Royal Air Force in the mid-1930s to facilitate 'scanning': see Basic Tee.

Basic Tee: a 1950s development of the Basic Six for civil aviation in which airspeed, attitude director (ADI) and altimeter form the top of the T and with the horizontal situation indicator (HSI) below the ADI.

'Blind' flying: flight without reference to the horizon or the surface of the earth: see Instrument Flight.

'Bone Dome': a pilot's protective helmet which includes a visor, microphone and headphones as well as oxygen mask: can also include a helmet mounted sight for aiming weapons.

Canopy: the transparent, movable enclosure of a cockpit.

Cathode Ray Tube (CRT): one of the primary methods of displaying information in the cockpit.

Central Flying School of the RAF: responsible for setting standard procedures for handling different aircraft types and for training instructors.

Centralized Warning: an attention-getting panel whose indications direct the crew to attend to a specific system.

Check Lists: lists of vital control actions for different phases of flight such as take-off.

Coaming: a shelf above the main instrument panels designed to limit the amount of external light falling on the instruments.

Constant Speed Propeller: a propeller in which the pitch of the blades is adjusted automatically to keep engine RPM at a pre-selected value.

Control Pedestal: the surfaces between the pilots on which are mounted the thrust, flap, undercarriage, trim, communication and other controls.

Contact Flying: maintaining control and navigating by reference to visible ground features as opposed to Instrument Flying.

Counter-pointer: an instrument whose information is conveyed by both a pointer moving over a scale and by numeral counters.

Cowling Gills: variable openings used for controlling the amount of cooling air passing over the cylinders of a piston engine.

Data Bus: in digital electronics, a group of parallel wires which carry 'bits' of data to and from different electronic systems.

Decca: a radio navigation system introduced in Europe at the end of the Second World War: one of the first 'map' type displays of aircraft position.

Deduced reckoning (DR): a navigational procedure which deduces position from known facts, such as speed and elapsed time, and assumed facts, such as wind speed and direction.

Digital: referring to computer systems: as opposed to analogue.

Direction Finding (DF): a radio method of determining the position of an aircraft relative to one or more radio stations or beacons.

Direct Voice Input (DVI): control of aircraft systems effected by voice commands.

Direct Voice Output (DVO): information and advice conveyed to the pilot through synthesized or recorded verbal message produced by computer-based systems.

Ejection Seat: a pilot's seat which can be ejected from an aircraft by an explosive charge.

Electronic displays: these include colour CRTs, arrays of LEDs, LCDs and other forms of solid-state technology and which in the 1980s were rapidly superseding electro-mechanical instruments.

Ergonomics: the study of the relationships between man and machines directed at providing the most effective methods of control and of imparting information.

Eye point: the reference position for determining arcs-of-view through the windscreen and the visibility of instruments when the pilot is seated.

Flight Deck: usually refers to a civil aircraft cockpit with positions for more than one pilot and other crew members.

Flight Engineer: a professional member of the flight deck responsible for the detail control of the engines and systems: Systems Engineer.

Flight Instruments: those instruments essential for the control of speed, attitude, vertical speed, altitude and heading.

Flight Management System: a computer-based system which commands the AFCS and the thrust control system so as to achieve a specific flight path, both horizontally and vertically between selected waypoints: it integrates the functions of navigation, performance management and flight planning and provides three-dimensional guidance and control.

Fly-by-Wire (FBW): a system of primary control which dispenses with direct mechanical links between the pilot's primary 'hand' controls and the control surfaces: the control surface actuators respond to electrical signals generated by a digital computer: the pilot commands the computer, the computer flies the aircraft.

Glide Slope: the nominal approach path in the vertical plane: in civil aviation this is an angle nominally of three degrees from the horizontal: the angle of the vertical component of an instrument landing system (ILS): in modern aviation the use of 'Glide' in the title is an anachronism.

G: gravity: specifically the effects of gravity on aircrew and airframe induced by manoeuvres.

GLOC: gravity effects which cause loss of consciousness.

Ground Roll Monitor (GRM): speed and distance remaining on the runway: used when the pilot takes over from an automatic landing sequence once the aircraft has touched down.

Gyroscopic effects: specifically referring to rotary-engine aircraft of the First World War era in which the heavy spinning mass of the engine affected control of an aircraft.

Gyro Gun Sight: a reflector sight in which the aiming symbols are displaced by a system of gyros so as to allow for the necessary aim-off or 'lead'.

HUD: Head Up Display: an electronic combined with optical system which projects information into the pilot's forward line of sight.

Horizontal Situation Indicator (HSI): one of the primary flight instruments: presents a 'map' picture of the aircraft in relation to navigational aids: can include weather radar display.

HOTAS: hands on throttle and stick: by concentrating essential controls on the throttle and on the control column the pilot of a combat aircraft can keep his hands on the primary controls during periods of high workload and high G.

Human Component: a control interface, such as a cockpit; has two principal elements or components — the human and the machine.

ICAO: International Civil Aviation Organisation: provides internationally acceptable standards of performance and operating procedures for all aspects of civil aviation.

Inertial Navigation (IN): a system of sensors, such as gyros, accelerometers or lasers, which continuously detects aircraft movement from a known position and displays the geographical coordinates of position.

Inside Looking Out: a fundamental instrument display concept: used for artificial horizons and attitude directors so that the symbols depicting the aircraft are fixed relative to the real aircraft and the symbols representing the real world outside the aircraft move.

Instrument Landing System (ILS): a system of radio beams which provide a glide slope and localizer reference to which an aircraft's ILS receivers respond and operate a cockpit indicator of 'fly right or left, fly up or down' and which, when followed by the pilot, keeps the aircraft on the correct path to a landing.

Institute of Aviation Medicine (IAM): an RAF institute dedicated to studying the medical and psychological aspects of flight.

Interface: an imaginary boundary between the human and the machine elements of a control position.

Knot: the international unit of aircraft

speed: one knot equals one nautical mile per hour: to convert knots to mph multiply by 1.15.

Lateral Preferences, Human: right-handedness for example.

Lateral reference: a part of the aircraft's structure, such as the cockpit coaming, used to hold zero or some required angle of bank.

LCD: liquid crystal display: used to form electronic instrument displays.

LED: light emitting diode: used in arrays to form electronic instruments.

Link: one of the first production standard flight simulators.

Lorenz: one of the first instrument landing systems: a system of radio guidance beams which provided the pilot with an aural indication of whether an aircraft was on the centre line leading to the airfield or was to the left or right and how far from touch down: it did not provide glide slope information: superseded by ILS.

Luftwaffe: air force: specifically the German Air Force founded in 1935.

Mach number: speed expressed as a proportion of the speed of sound in air, this varies with altitude and temperature: at 15 degrees Celsius and at sea level the speed of sound is 670 knots. Therefore, for example, Mach 0.8 at sea level = 0.8 × 670 = 536 knots

Mnemonics: aids to completing a cockpit check: for example c.1940 HTMPFG Hydraulics, Throttle friction, Mixture, Propeller Pitch, Flaps and Fuel cocks, engine cooling Gills.

MFD (Multi Function Display): an electronic, colour, display whose format and information can be selected by the pilot to match the requirements of a particular phase of flight or function.

Nautical Mile (nm): the average length of one minute of latitude (6,080 feet): the basic aviation unit of distance.

North East Corridor: the civil airways system extending NE from Washington DC to Boston Mass in which the density of traffic in the late 1940s caused problems for both pilots and controllers.

Pilot Associate: a computer-based system which advises, prompts and warns the human pilot.

Pointer on Dial: an instrument whose information is conveyed by a pointer moving across a circular scale.

Popham Panel: a cloth panel whose shape and symbols could be varied to convey different messages to a pilot flying overhead: used by the RAF for ground-to-air communication.

Power Controls: a system of hydraulic or electric actuators which operate the primary control surfaces, thereby reducing the physical effort of the pilot.

Radar altimeter: an alternative to the pressure altimeter.

RMI: Radio Magnetic Indicator.

Radio Range: a system of radio beams providing A .— and N —. Morse signals and an overlap to form a beam: if a pilot heard As he was to the left of the beam, if Ns he was to the right, and a steady note indicated he was on the beam.

Reflector sight: a system of collimating lenses and combining glass which projects aiming symbology into the pilot's line-of-sight focused at infinity.

RNAS. Royal Naval Air Service: along with the RFC formed the RAF on the 1st April 1918.

RFC: Royal Flying Corps

Roll, pitch and yaw: the three axis around which an aircraft is manoeuvred: roll (ailerons) = banking so that the wings are at an angle to the horizon: pitch (elevator) = tilting the aircraft's nose above or below the horizon: yaw: (rudder) = changing the heading of the aircraft's nose without using bank.

Side-stick control: positioning the primary control of ailerons and elevator at the side of the pilot instead of between his knees.

Situational Awareness: the pilot's awareness of the total situation in which he is flying: it includes both 'internal' and 'external' information i.e. the performance and potential of the aircraft as well as all external factors such as hostile elements in the air space surrounding the aircraft.

Spinner: a streamlined fairing of the hub of a propeller.

Stalling: flying an aircraft at an attitude, angle of attack or speed at which the wings are unable to produce the required lift.

Symbionics: a word derived from symbiosis, electronics and biology: electronic systems which mutually support each other and which have the characteristics of living systems.

Threshold: the first part of a runway in the direction of landing: the ideal touchdown point will be 800 feet or more further on.

Torque effects: the tendency in a propeller-driven aircraft for the aircraft to rotate in the opposite direction to that of the propeller.

Up-front control panel: concentrating all primary and vital selector buttons immediately below the HUD.

USAAF: United States Army Air Force, the precursor of the United States Air Force.

USMC: United States Marine Corps.

Vertical Speed Indicator (VSI): one of the primary flight instruments: graduated in hundreds of feet or metres per minute.

VOR: VHF Omni Range (Radio beacon).

Waypoint: a predetermined and known geographical position forming a stage at the end of a route segment: in military aviation a point in space to which an aircraft may be vectored.

Weather radar: a CRT display, sometimes combined with the HSI, to indicate different levels of precipitation and storm cells.

Workload: a qualitative and quantitative measure of a pilot's mental and physical work: used in the design of the cockpit, navigational and ATC systems to ensure that controls and instruments and procedures do not increase the workload level excessively.

Zero Reader: specifically the Sperry 'command' type instrument whose indications enabled a pilot to 'capture' and keep to the glide slope and localizer beams of an ILS.

Zogging: specifically arm and hand signals used to convey information: used at one time by RAF crews in the absence of radio.

BIBLIOGRAPHY

R. Barker, *The Schneider Trophy Races* (Chatto and Windus 1971)

C. Babington-Smith, *Amy Johnson* (Collins 1977)

S.R. Broadbent, *Jane's Avionics 1987–88* (Jane's Publishing 1988)

E. Brown, *Wings of the Weird and Wonderful* (Airlife 1983)

Birch and Bramson, *Flight Briefing for Pilots* (Longman 1981)

Bridgeman and Stewart, *The Clouds Remember* (not known)

D.L. Brown, *Miles Aircraft* (Putnam 1970)

D. Beaty, *The Water Jump* (Secker and Warburg 1976)

J.F. Bowyer, *Interceptor Fighters* (Patrick Stevens Ltd 1984)

R. Chandler, *Off the Beam* (David Rendel 1970)

R.A. Chorley, 'Seventy Years of Instruments and Displays', 3rd Folland Lecture, Royal Aeronautical Society, February 1976

L.F.E. Coombs, 'The Pilot's Place', *Flight International*, 25 January 1957

'Right and Left Hand Dominance in Navigation', *The Journal of Navigation*, Vol 25, 3 pp 359–369, 1972

'Front Office Evolution', *Air International* series, February 1972 et seq.

'Flight Deck Evolution', *Interavia* series, vol 27, 7, p774, 1973 et seq.

'The Influence of Human Laterality on the Design and Operation of Vehicles': Unpublished thesis University of Surrey, 1973.

'Left and Right in Cockpit Evolution', *Journal of the Royal Aeronautical Society*, November 1974, pp 513–522.

'Cockpits of the RAF', *Aeroplane Monthly* series, October 1983 et seq.

D.P. Davies, *Handling the Big Jets* (ARB 1968)

R.E.G. Davies, *A History of the World's Airlines* (OUP 1964)

R.E. Gillman, *Croydon to Concorde* (Murray 1980)

C. Gibbs-Smith, *The Aeroplane: An Historical Survey*, HMSO 1960

J. Goulding, *Interceptor* (Ian Allan 1986)

Green and Swanborough, *Fighters* (Salamander 1981)

W.T. Gunston, *Attack Aircraft of the West* (Ian Allan 1974)

Gunston and Spick, *Modern Air Combat* (Salamander 1983)

Haddow and Grosz *The German Giants* (Putnam 1962)

M. Hirst, 'Cockpit Paraphanalia for Pilots' Military Technology', June 1983

'Avionics Analysed' *Air International* series, Janaury 1983 et seq.

K. Huenecke, *Modern Combat Aircraft Design* (English edition ed. L.F.E. Coombs) (Airlife 1987)

R. Hurst (ed), *Pilot Error* (Crosby, Lockwood Staples 1976)

L.S. Hobbs 'The Wright Brothers Engines and their Design', Smithsonian Annals of Flight No 5, 1971

A. Imrie, *Pictorial History of the German Army Air Service* (Ian Allan 1971)

D.D. Jackson, *Flying the Mails* (Time Life 1982)

A.J. Jackson, *Avro Aircraft since 1908* (Putnam 1965)

R. Jackson, *The Sky Their Frontier* (Airlife 1983)

J. Jewell, *Engineering for Life* (Martin Baker 1979)

D. Jones, *The Time Shrinkers* (David Rendel 1971)

H.F. King, *Armament of British Aircraft* (Putnam 1971)

F.C. Kelly, *The Wright Brothers* (Panther 1958)

D. Lee, *Never Stop the Engine When It's Hot* (Harmsworth 1983)

P. Lewis, *The British Fighter Since 1912* (Putnam 1967)
The British Bomber since 1914 (Putnam 1980)

C. Lindbergh, *Spirit of St Louis* (Charles Scribner's Sons)

Sir Arthur Longmore, *From Sea to Sky* (Geoffrey Bles 1946)

E.J. Lovesey, 'The Instrument Explosion', *Applied Ergonomics*, March 1977.

M.W. MacFarland, *The Papers of Orville and Wilbur Wright* (McGraw Hill 1953)

D. Middleton, *Test Pilots* (Guild Publishing 1985)

W. Murray, *Luftwaffe* (Allen and Unwin 1985)

W.C. Ocker, 'Instrument Flying to Combat Fog', *Scientific American* pp 430–432, December 1930.

C.A. Owens, *Flight Operations* (Granada 1982)

R.B. Parke, *The Pilot Maker* (Gossett and Dunlap 1970)

J. Quill, *Spitfire* (Murray 1983)

T.T. Paterson, *Morale in War and Work* (Max Parrish 1955)

H. Penrose, *British Aviation: Ominous Skies 1935–39* (RAF Museum 1980)

J. Pudney, *The Camel Fighter* (Hamish Hamilton 1964)

I. Reinecke, *Electronic Illusions* (Penguin 1984)

Q. Reynolds, *The Amazing Mr Doolittle* (Appleton, Century Crofts Inc 1953)

P. Richey, *Fighter Pilot* (Batsford 1941)

A. Robinson, *In the Cockpit* (Orbis 1979)

D.H. Robinson, *The Dangerous Sky* (Foulis 1973)

J.M. Rolfe, 'Fighter Aircraft Cockpits', (RAF Institute of Aviation Medicine Report No 222 1964)

A. St Exupery, *Wind, Sand and Stars* (Heinemann 1935)

J.D. Stevenson, *Aircraft Gyroscopic Flight Instruments* (Sperry 1969)

C.J. Stewart, *Aircraft Instruments* (Chapman and Hall 1930)

S. Stewert, *Flying the Big Jets* (Airlife 1986)

M. Siberry, *Instruments of Flight* (David and Charles 1974)

John Stroud, 'Wings of Peace', *Aeroplane Monthly* series, October 1983 et seq.

P. Townsend, *Duel of Eagles* (Wiedenfeld and Nicholson)

H.A. Taylor, *Test Pilot at War* (Ian Allan 1970)

O. Thetford, *Aircraft of the Royal Air Force* (Putnam 1957)

G. Wallace, *RAF Biggin Hill* (Putnam 1957)

V.M. Yeates, *Winged Victory* (Jonathan Cape 1934)

INDEX

Page numbers in *italics* refer to pages which also have illustrations.